Study Guide to accompany

DRUGS AND SOCIETY
Ninth Edition

Glen R. Hanson
Peter J. Venturelli
Annette E. Fleckenstein

JONES AND BARTLETT PUBLISHERS
Sudbury, Massachusetts
BOSTON   TORONTO   LONDON   SINGAPORE

World Headquarters
Jones and Bartlett Publishers
40 Tall Pine Drive
Sudbury, MA 01776
978-443-5000
info@jbpub.com
www.jbpub.com

Jones and Bartlett Publishers Canada
6339 Ormindale Way
Mississauga, Ontario L5V 1J2
CANADA

Jones and Bartlett Publishers International
Barb House, Barb Mews
London W6 7PA
UK

Jones and Bartlett's books and products are available through most bookstores and online booksellers. To contact Jones and Bartlett Publishers directly, call 800-832-0034, fax 978-443-8000, or visit our website, www.jbpub.com.

Substantial discounts on bulk quantities of Jones and Bartlett's publications are available to corporations, professional associations, and other qualified organizations. For details and specific discount information, contact the special sales department at Jones and Bartlett via the above contact information or send an email to specialsales@jbpub.com.

Production Credits
Acquisitions Editor: Jacqueline Mark-Geraci
Senior Production Editor: Julie C. Bolduc
Associate Editor: Nicole L. Quinn
Editorial Assistant: Amy L. Flagg
Associate Marketing Manager: Wendy Thayer
Manufacturing Buyer: Therese Connell
Composition: Shawn Girsberger
Cover Design: Kristin E. Ohlin
Cover Image: © Jeremy Woodhouse/Photodisc/Getty Images
Printing and Binding: Courier Stoughton
Cover Printing: Courier Stoughton

ISBN-13: 978-0-7637-3755-9
ISBN-10: 0-7637-3755-0

6048
Printed in the United States of America
10 09 08 07 06   10 9 8 7 6 5 4 3 2

Contents

Introduction

The impact of drug use and/or abuse on the lives of ordinary people is a topic that is important and complex enough to study for an entire semester. For some students this course is required to fulfill degree requirements for graduation; others choose this as an elective. Most students are surprised at the volume of information covered in a course on drugs and society, and sometimes do not appreciate the multiple dimensions and body of knowledge until after the first quiz or exam.

Each of us brings unique backgrounds, experiences, values, and beliefs to discussions of drug issues. These factors influence your decision-making in a variety of ways.

In this course, you will gain a real perspective of drug-related problems in our society. No matter your discipline, in this course, you will find useful current information and perspectives to help you understand:

- Social and psychological reasons why drug use and abuse occur
- The results of drug use and abuse
- How to prevent drug use and abuse
- How drugs can be used effectively for therapeutic purposes

The knowledge gained in this course can both protect and enhance your life.

This study guide is designed to help you organize and reinforce your learning about the issues covered in *Drugs and Society*. The following features can be found in each of the chapters:

- **Chapter Outlines** Give you an idea of the topics covered in each chapter.
- **Self-Tests** Test your knowledge of the reading and give you a chance to revisit concepts. Each chapter contains all or some of the following: Key Terms, Fill-in-the-Blank, Identify, Matching, True/False, and Discussion Questions.
- **Lecture Slides** Help you to have organized notes, which is essential at exam time and when doing assignments.

Lecture Slides

The lecture slide component is located at the end of each chapter and contains the full set of PowerPoint slides that accompany your textbook, as well as space next to each slide for you to jot down the terms and concepts that you feel are most important to each lecture. This guide will save you from having to write down everything that is on the slides. Do the assigned reading, listen in lecture, follow the key points your instructor makes, and write down meaningful notes. This is the perfect place to write down questions that you want to ask your professor later or reminders to yourself to go back and study a certain concept again to make sure you really got it.

For more information on the most effective note-taking methods that will save you both time and effort when reviewing for exams, see the Note-Taking Tips section directly following this Introduction.

Once the lecture slides component of this Study Guide has helped to organize and simplify your notes on each chapter, the self-tests will assess how well you have mastered the material. Your ability to easily locate the important concepts of a recent lecture and test yourself on the most important points and terminology will prove to be essential at exam time.

This Study Guide is a valuable resource. You've found a wonderful study partner!

Note-Taking Tips

1. It is easier to take notes if you are not hearing the information for the first time. Read the chapter or the material that is about to be discussed before class. This will help you to anticipate what will be said in class, and have an idea of what to write down. It will also help to read over your notes from the last class. This way you can avoid having to spend the first few minutes of class trying to remember where you left off last time.

2. Don't waste your time trying to write down everything that your professor says. Instead, listen closely and only write down the important points. Review these important points after class to help remind you of related points that were made during the lecture.

3. If the class discussion takes a spontaneous turn, pay attention and participate in the discussion. Only take notes on the conclusions that are relevant to the lecture.

4. Emphasize main points in your notes. You may want to use a highlighter, special notation (asterisks, exclamation points), format (circle, underline), or placement on the page (indented, bulleted). You will find that when you try to recall these points, you will be able to actually picture them on the page.

5. Be sure to copy down word-for-word specific formulas, laws, and theories.

6. Hearing something repeated, stressed, or summed up can be a signal that it is an important concept to understand.

7. Organize handouts, study guides, and exams in your notebook along with your lecture notes. It may be helpful to use a three-ring binder, so that you can insert pages wherever you need to.

8. When taking notes, you might find it helpful to leave a wide margin on all four sides of the page. Doing this allows you to note names, dates, definitions, etc. for easy access and studying later. It may also be helpful to make notes of questions you want to ask your professor about or research later, ideas or relationships that you want to explore more on your own, or concepts that you don't fully understand.

9. It is best to maintain a separate notebook for each class. Labeling and dating your notes can be helpful when you need to look up information from previous lectures.

10. Make your notes legible, and take notes directly in your notebook. Chances are you won't recopy them no matter how noble your intentions. Spend the time you would have spent recopying the notes studying them instead, drawing conclusions and making connections that you didn't have time for in class.

11. Look over your notes after class while the lecture is still fresh in your mind. Fix illegible items and clarify anything you don't understand. Do this again right before the next class.

CHAPTER 1

Introduction to Drugs and Society

◎ Chapter Outline

The chapter outline provides you with an organizational guide to the topics and ideas presented in this chapter of the text.

Introduction
Drug Use
Dimensions of Drug Use
  Most Commonly Abused Drugs
An Overview of Drugs in Society
  How Widespread Is Drug Abuse?
  Extent and Frequency of Drug Use in Society
  Current Patterns of Licit and Illicit Drug Use
  Types of Drug Users
  Influence of the Mass Media on Drug Use

Drug Use and Drug Dependence
  When Does Drug Use Lead to Abuse
  Drug Dependence
The Costs of Drug Use to Society
  Drugs, Crime, and Violence
  Drugs in the Workplace: A Costly Affliction
**Venturing to a Higher Form of Consciousness:
The Holistic Self-Awareness Approach to
Drug Use**

◎ Key Terms

Define the following terms:

1. Drug _____

2. Addiction _____

3. Gateway drug _____

4. OTC drugs _____

5. Ethanol _____

6. EAPs _____

7. Equal-opportunity affliction _____

◎ Fill-in-the-Blank

1. _____ are drugs that result from altered chemical structures of current illicit drugs.

2. The unintentional or inappropriate use of prescribed or over-the-counter (OTC) types of drugs is known as _____.

3. _____ refers to the need to continue taking a drug to avoid withdrawal symptoms.

4. _____ are drug compounds that affect the central nervous system and alter consciousness and/or perceptions.

5. Coffee, tea, alcohol, tobacco, and over-the-counter drugs are all examples of _____ drugs. Marijuana, cocaine, and LSD are all _____ drugs.

6. _____ are new drugs that are developed by people intending to circumvent the illegality of a drug by modifying a drug into a new compound. An example of this kind of drug is _____.

7. The _____ is the principal federal agency for enforcing U.S. drug laws.

8. Drug testing may be administered in three ways:

   1. _____
   2. _____
   3. _____

◎ Identify

1. Identify the three categories of drug users and explain characteristics of each.

   a. _____
   b. _____
   c. _____

2. Identify and describe the five phases of addiction.

   a. _____
   b. _____
   c. _____
   d. _____
   e. _____

3. Identify the four principal factors that affect drug use and explain each one.

a. _____

b. _____

c. _____

d. _____

4. Identify four symptoms of withdrawal.

a. _____

b. _____

c. _____

d. _____

5. Identify and define Erich Goode's four types of drug use.

a. _____

b. _____

c. _____

d. _____

6. Identify five reasons why people take drugs.

a. _____

b. _____

c. _____

d. _____

e. _____

◎ Discussion Questions

1. Describe the holistic self-awareness approach to drug use. Discuss your thoughts on this approach and

its effectiveness in drug abuse treatment. _____

_____

_____

2. What is drug misuse? Provide multiple examples of how one might misuse a drug. _____

_____

_____

3. How does the mass media affect drug use? _____

_____

_____

Notes

NINTH EDITION

Glen R. Hanson
Peter J. Venturelli
Annette E. Fleckenstein

Drugs and **Society**

Introduction to Drugs and Society

Chapter 1

Key Concerns of Chapter 1

- What constitutes a drug?
- What are the most commonly abused drugs?
- What are designer drugs?
- How widespread is drug use?
- What is the extent and frequency of drug use in our society?
- What are the current statistics and trends in drug use?

Key Concerns of Chapter 1 (continued)

- What types of drug users exist?
- How does the media influence drug use?
- What attracts people to drug use
- When does drug use lead to drug dependence?
- At what point does drug addiction set in?
- What are the costs of drug addiction to society?
- What can be gained by learning about the complexity of drug use and abuse?

Notes

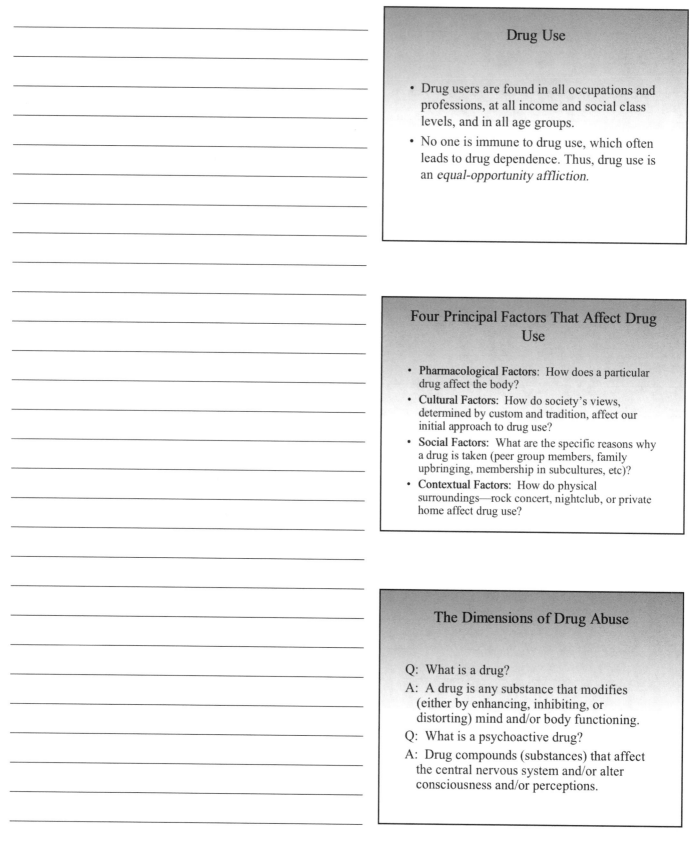

Drug Use

- Drug users are found in all occupations and professions, at all income and social class levels, and in all age groups.
- No one is immune to drug use, which often leads to drug dependence. Thus, drug use is an *equal-opportunity affliction.*

Four Principal Factors That Affect Drug Use

- **Pharmacological Factors:** How does a particular drug affect the body?
- **Cultural Factors:** How do society's views, determined by custom and tradition, affect our initial approach to drug use?
- **Social Factors:** What are the specific reasons why a drug is taken (peer group members, family upbringing, membership in subcultures, etc)?
- **Contextual Factors:** How do physical surroundings—rock concert, nightclub, or private home affect drug use?

The Dimensions of Drug Abuse

Q: What is a drug?

A: A drug is any substance that modifies (either by enhancing, inhibiting, or distorting) mind and/or body functioning.

Q: What is a psychoactive drug?

A: Drug compounds (substances) that affect the central nervous system and/or alter consciousness and/or perceptions.

Notes

Psychoactive Drugs

- Psychoactive drugs are classified as either:
  - Licit (Legal)
    - Examples may include coffee, tea, alcohol, tobacco, and over-the-counter drugs.
  - Illicit (Illegal)
    - Examples may include marijuana, cocaine, LSD, etc.

Most Commonly Abused Types of Drugs

- Alcohol (ethanol)
- Tobacco (all forms of tobacco)
- Stimulants
  - Amphetamines, Cocaine, "Crack," Caffeine, Nicotine
- Hallucinogens
  - LSD, Mescaline, Peyote
- Depressants
  - Barbiturates, Benzodiazepines, Methaqualone, Alcohol

Most Commonly Abused Types of Drugs
(continued)

- Cannabis
  - Marijuana and Hashish
- Anabolic Steroids
  - A synthetic form of the male hormone testosterone
- Inhalants/Organic Solvents
  - Inhalants such as gasoline, model glue, paint thinner, as well as certain foods, herbs, and vitamins
- Narcotics
  - Opium, Morphine, Codeine, and Heroin

Notes

_____

_____

_____

_____

_____

_____

_____

_____

_____

_____

_____

_____

_____

_____

_____

_____

_____

_____

_____

_____

_____

_____

_____

_____

Designer Drugs/Synthetic Drugs or Synthetic Opioids

- **Structural analogs** are drugs that result from altered chemical structures of current illicit drugs.
  - Involves modifying the basic molecular skeleton of a compound to form a new molecular species.
- **Designer drugs** /synthetic drugs or synthetic opioids
  - New categories of hybrid drugs, e.g., Ecstasy
  - These relatively recent types of drugs are created as structural analogs of substances already classified under the Controlled Substances Act.

Gateway Drugs

- **Gateway drugs** are types of drugs that are believed to lead to using other more powerfully mind-altering and addictive drugs, such as hallucinogens, cocaine, "crack," and heroin.
  - Alcohol, tobacco, and marijuana are the most commonly used gateway drugs.

Drug Misuse

- **Drug misuse** is the unintentional or inappropriate use of prescribed or over-the-counter (OTC) types of drugs.

Notes

Six Examples of Drug Misuse

- Taking more drugs than prescribed
- Using OTC or psychoactive drugs in excess without medical supervision
- Mixing drugs with alcohol or other types of drugs
- Using old medicines to self-treat new symptoms of an illness
- Discontinuing prescribed drugs at will and/or against physician's orders
- Administering prescribed drugs to a family member without medical consultation and supervision

Dimensions of Drug Abuse

- **Drug abuse** is the willful misuse of either licit or illicit drugs for the purpose of recreation, perceived necessity, or convenience.
  - Drug abuse refers to a more intense misuse of drugs—often to the point of addiction
  - Also known as *chemical* or *substance* abuse

Erich Goode's Four Types of Drug Use

- **Legal instrumental use**—taking prescribed drugs or OTC drugs to relieve or treat mental or physical symptoms
- **Legal recreational use**—using licit drugs like tobacco, alcohol, and caffeine to achieve a certain mental state
- **Illegal instrumental use**—taking nonprescribed drugs to achieve a task or goal
- **Illegal recreational use**—taking illicit drugs for fun or pleasure

Notes

_____

_____

_____

_____

_____

_____

_____

_____

_____

_____

_____

_____

_____

_____

_____

_____

_____

_____

_____

_____

_____

_____

_____

_____

Drug Use: Statistics and Trends

- Social drugs
  - $104 billion for alcohol
  - $51.9 billion for cigarettes
  - $2 billion for cigars; chewing, pipe, roll-your-own tobacco, and snuff
  - $5.7 billion for coffee, teas, and cocoa
- Prescription drugs
  - $430 billion worldwide and $176 billion in the U.S.

Drug Use: Statistics and Trends
(continued)

- OTC drugs
  - $23.5 billion
- Nonmedical use of prescription drugs
  - In 2001, 16% of Americans 12 or older (36 million) had misused prescription drugs at least once in their lifetime
- Miscellaneous drugs (such as aerosols, nutmeg, morning glory seeds, etc.)
  - Amount unknown

Drug Quiz (according to the research studies reported in your textbook)

Q: How many Americans, age 12 and up, have used alcohol in the past month?

A: 119 million

Q: How many Americans in the past month have smoked tobacco?

A: 60 million

Q: How many Americans use or have used marijuana in their lifetime?

A: 97 million (41%)

Q: How many drugs can be found in the average household?

A: 50 drugs (40% prescriptions, 60% OTC)

Notes

National Household Survey on Drug Abuse, 2003

- 198 million Americans used alcohol during their lifetime
- 163 million Americans used cigarettes
- 110 million Americans used any illicit drug(s)

Most commonly used illicit drugs (lifetime use):

- 41% used marijuana (6.2% used in last month)
- 15% used hallucinogens
- 20% used a psychotherapeutic drug(s) for nonmedical reason(s) (2.7% used in last month)
- 15% used cocaine

Drug Use: Other Major Findings

Age Patterns: 18–25 age category report the most illicit drug use

Racial and Ethnic Differences (highest rates of use, past month):

American Indian/Alaska Native 12.1%
Two or more races 12%
Black 8.7%
White 8.3%
Hispanic or Latino 8%

Drug Use: Other Major Findings
(continued)

Gender

- Boys have a greater increase in the percentage of illicit drug use than girls.
- Men are more likely to report current drug use than women

Pregnant Women

- Pregnant women are less likely to use drugs than similar age women who are not pregnant.

Notes

_____

_____

_____

_____

_____

_____

_____

_____

_____

_____

_____

_____

_____

_____

_____

_____

_____

_____

_____

_____

_____

_____

_____

_____

_____

_____

_____

_____

Drug Use: Other Major Findings
(continued)

Education: College graduates (5.2%) had the lowest rate of current use, while those who did not complete high school (9%) had the highest use of illicit drugs.

Employment: Unemployed persons (18.2%) have a greater tendency to use more illicit-types of drugs than people gainfully employed (7.9% full-time and 10.7% part-time workers).

Drug Use: Other Major Findings
(continued)

Geography: The rate of illicit drug use is highest in large metropolitan areas for the general population.

Criminal Justice: 33% of state prisoners and 22% of federal prisoners reported that they had committed their offenses while under the influence of drugs.

Three Types of Drug Users

- Experimenters
  - Begin using drugs largely because of peer pressure and curiosity, and they confine their use to recreational settings.
- Compulsive users
  - Devote considerable time and energy into getting high, talk incessantly (sometimes exclusively) about drug use, and become connoisseurs of street drugs.
- Floaters or "chippers"
  - Focus more on using other people's drugs without maintaining as much of a personal supply.

Notes

Media Influence on Drug Use

- The alcohol industry spends more than $1 billion on yearly advertising
- The advertising budget for Budweiser beer exceeds the entire budget for research on alcoholism and alcohol abusers
- Spending on consumer advertising for prescription drugs was $1.8 billion in 1999
- Since the "Friends Don't Let Friends Drive Drunk" Ad Council campaign began, 79% of Americans have stopped a friend from getting behind the wheel while intoxicated

Why Are People So Attracted to Drugs?

People use drugs as a means to temporarily:
- Experience pleasure or heighten good feelings.
- Relieve stress, tension, or anxiety.
- Forget one's problems and avoid or postpone worries.
- Relax after a tension-filled day of work.
- Fit in with peers or as a rite of passage.
- Enhance religious or mystical experiences.
- Relieve pain and some symptoms of illness.

When Does Use Lead to Abuse?

- The *amount* of drug taken does not necessarily determine abuse.
- The *motive* for taking the drug is the most important factor in determining presence of abuse.
- Initial drug abuse symptoms include:
  - Excessive use
  - Constant preoccupation about the availability and supply of the drug
  - Refusal to admit excessive use
  - Reliance on the drug

Notes

_____

_____

_____

_____

_____

_____

_____

_____

_____

_____

_____

_____

_____

_____

_____

_____

_____

_____

_____

_____

_____

_____

_____

_____

Drug Dependence

Both physical and psychological factors precipitate drug dependence:

- **Physical dependence** refers to the need to continue taking the drug to avoid withdrawal symptoms, which often include feelings of discomfort and illness.
- **Psychological dependence** refers to the need that a user may feel for continued use of a drug in order to experience its effects and/or relieve withdrawal symptoms.

Stages of Drug Dependence

- **Relief**—satisfaction from negative feelings in using the drug
- **Increased use**—involves taking greater quantities of the drug
- **Preoccupation**—consists of a constant concern with the substance
- **Dependency**—a synonym for addiction, is when more of the drug is sought despite the presence of physical symptoms
- **Withdrawal**—the physical and/or psychological effects from not using the drug

Costs of Drug Use to Society

- Illness
- Shortened lifespan
- Broken home
- Fetal alcohol syndrome
- Criminal behavior
- Drugs in the workplace
- Cost of Assistance programs (e.g., Employee Assistance Programs [EAPs])

Notes

Costs of Drug Use to Society Statistics

- The National Institute on Drug Abuse (NIDA) estimates that the typical narcotic habit costs $100/day
- A heroin addict must steal three to five times the actual cost of the drugs to maintain a habit—about $100k per year
- Three out of four prostitutes in major cities have a serious drug dependency

Drugs in the Workplace

- Illicit drug use costs American businesses billions of dollars annually in lost productivity and increased healthcare costs
- 65.6% of full-time workers reported alcohol use within the past month
- 7% reported illicit drug use in the past month
- 9.7% of full-time workers reported marijuana use within the past year

Drug Testing

- Used to identify those who may be using drugs
- Urine, blood screening, or hair analysis

Duration of Detection /"Cut-Off" Levels

Urine Analysis:

- Amphetamines—24–72 hours
- Cocaine/Metabolite—24–72 hours
- Opiates—24–72 hours
- PCP—24–96 hours
- THC/Metabolite—24 hours–3 weeks (depends on frequency of use)

Note: Hair analysis 1 to 3 months for all drugs listed above

Notes

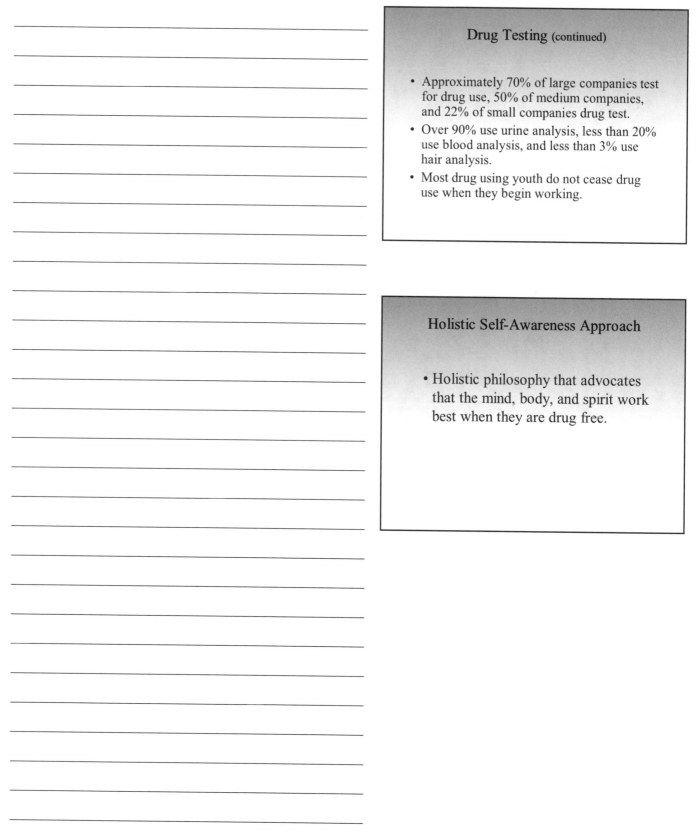

Drug Testing (continued)

- Approximately 70% of large companies test for drug use, 50% of medium companies, and 22% of small companies drug test.
- Over 90% use urine analysis, less than 20% use blood analysis, and less than 3% use hair analysis.
- Most drug using youth do not cease drug use when they begin working.

Holistic Self-Awareness Approach

- Holistic philosophy that advocates that the mind, body, and spirit work best when they are drug free.

CHAPTER 2

Explaining Drug Use and Abuse

◎ Chapter Outline

The chapter outline provides you with an organizational guide to the topics and ideas presented in this chapter of the text.

◎ Key Terms

Define the following terms:

1. Psychoanalysis _____

2. "Double wall" of encapsulation _____

3. Neurotransmitters _____

4. Habituation _____

5. Master status _____

6. Subculture theory _____

7. Conventional behavior _____

8. Control theory _____

◎ Fill-in-the-Blank

1. The belief that people abuse alcohol because they choose to do so defines the _____ _____ of addiction.

2. The _____ is one of the major divisions of the nervous system, composed of the brain and the spinal cord.

3. The brain transmitter believed to mediate the rewarding aspects of most drugs of abuse is called _____ _____.

4. How drug substances alter and affect the brain's mental functions are known as _____ _____.

5. People who characteristically are continually seeking new or novel thrills in their experiences are known as _____.

6. The ratio between reinforcers, both favorable and disfavorable, for sustaining drug use behavior is called _____.

7. _____ is the theory emphasizing that other people's perceptions directly influence one's self-image.

8. The process of redefining a person in light of a major status position is known as _____ _____.

9. _____ is the growth and development process responsible for learning how to become a responsible, functioning human being.

◎ Identify

1. Identify and define three features usually present in substance dependence.

   a._____

   b. _____

   c. _____

2. Identify the three major models of addiction and briefly explain the beliefs of each model.

   a. _____

   b. _____

   c. _____

3. Identify five danger signals of drug use.

   a. _____

b. _____

c. _____

d. _____

e. _____

◎ Discussion Questions

1. Why are drug use and abuse even more serious issues now than they were in the past? Give three

possible reasons and discuss their significance. _____

_____

_____

2. Discuss the connection between psychiatric disorders and drug abuse. _____

_____

_____

3. Discuss some risk factors for the development of abuse. _____

_____

_____

4. Explain the difference between social influence theories and structural influence theories. Give an

example of each. _____

_____

_____

5. According to the labeling theory, what are the two types of deviance? Explain the difference between

the two. At what point does a person transition from one type of deviance to the other? _____

_____

_____

6. Discuss the importance of making low-risk drug choices. How might one maintain a low-risk approach

to drug use? _____

_____

_____

Notes

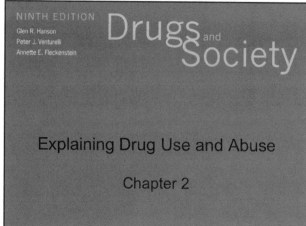

NINTH EDITION

Glen R. Hanson
Peter J. Venturelli
Annette E. Fleckenstein

Drugs and Society

Explaining Drug Use and Abuse

Chapter 2

Why Do People Use Drugs?

- Why do people subject their bodies and minds to the harmful effects of repetitive drug use, eventual addiction, and relapse back into drug use?
- Why is drug use a more serious problem than in the past?

Ten Reasons Why Drug Use Is More Serious Today

- Since the 1960s drug use is more widespread.
- Drugs are much more potent than they were years ago.
- Drug use remains extremely popular. Their sale is a multibillion dollar a year business, with major influence on many national economies.
- More so than years ago, both licit and illicit drugs are introduced and experimented with by youths at increasingly younger age. These drugs are often supplied by older siblings, friends, and acquaintances.

Notes

Ten Reasons Why Drug Use Is More Serious Today (continued)

- Through the media, people in today's society are more directly exposed to direct advertising of drugs.
- Greater availability and wider dissemination of drug information, e.g., spam emails, drug websites for purchasing prescription drugs without prescriptions, chat rooms, and best methods and instructions on how to make drugs.
- Crack as well as crystal methamphetamine and other manufactured "newer" drugs offer potent effects at low cost.

Ten Reasons Why Drug Use Is More Serious Today (continued)

- Drug use endangers the future of a society by harming its youth and potentially destroying the lives of many young men and women.
- Drug use and especially drug dealing are becoming major factors in the growth of crime rates among the young.
- Seven in ten drug users work full-time and this increases the possibility of serious accidents in the workplace.

Basic Reasons People Take Drugs

- Searching for pleasure
- Relieve stress, tension, or depression
- Peer pressure
- Enhance religious or mystical experiences
- Enhance social experiences
- Enhance work performance
- Relieve pain or symptoms of illness

Can you think of additional reasons not listed above?

Notes

_____

_____

_____

_____

_____

_____

_____

_____

_____

_____

_____

_____

_____

_____

_____

_____

_____

_____

_____

_____

_____

_____

_____

_____

Nature of Addiction

Should addiction be considered:
- A bad habit?
- A failure of healthy choices?
- A failure of morality?
- A symptom of other problems?
- A chronic disease?

Costs of Addiction

- Although public perception of drug abuse and addiction as a major social problem has waxed and waned over the past 20 years, the social costs of addiction have not.
- The total criminal justice, health insurance, and other costs in the United States are roughly estimated at $90 to $185 billion annually.

Defining Addiction

- The term **addiction** is derived from the Latin verb *addicere*, which refers to the process of binding to things.
- Addiction is a complex disease.
- Originally, the World Health Organization (WHO) defined it as "a state of periodic or chronic intoxication detrimental to the individual and society, which is characterized by an overwhelming desire to continue taking the drug and to obtain it by any means" (1964, pp. 9–10).

Notes

Addiction Includes Both Physical and Psychological Dependence

- **Physical** dependence is the body's need to constantly have the drug or drugs.
- **Psychological** dependence is the mental inability to stop using the drug or drugs.

Substance Abuse and Dependence
(from DSM-IV-TR, 4th Edition)

- **Substance abuse** is considered maladaptive, but it is carefully differentiated from true addiction.
- **Substance dependence** is true addiction, the essential feature of which is continued use despite significant substance-related problems known to user.

Physical/Psychological Dependence

- Significant substance-related problems experienced by the user, includes:
  - **Tolerance**—need for increased usage
  - **Withdrawal**—unpleasant physical and/or emotional symptoms experienced by the user when attempting to quit using a drug
  - **Compulsive**—increasing time spent in substance-related activities (obtaining and using, and recovering from drug effects)

Notes

_____

_____

_____

_____

_____

_____

_____

_____

_____

_____

_____

_____

_____

_____

_____

_____

_____

_____

_____

_____

_____

_____

_____

_____

Major Models of Addiction

- **Moral model**—poor morals and lifestyle—a choice
- **Disease model**—a belief that addiction is both chronic and progressive and that the drug user does not have control over the use and abuse of the drug
- **Character or personality predisposition model** —personality disorder—problems with the *personality* of the addicted

Career Pattern of Addiction

- Experimentation or initiation of drug use
- Escalation (increasing use)
- Maintenance—optimistic belief that the drug fits in well with day-to-day goals
- Dysfunction—problems with use interfering with day-to-day goals
- Recovery—getting out of drug use/abuse
- Exaddict—successfully quitting

Some Major Risk Factors for Addiction

- Alcohol and/or other drugs used alone
- Alcohol and/or other drugs used in order to help stress and/or anxiety
- Availability of drugs
- Abusive and/or neglectful parents; other dysfunctional family patterns
- Misperception of peer norms regarding the extent of alcohol and/or drug use
- Alienation factors: isolation, emptiness, etc.

Notes

Major Risk Factors for *Adolescents*

- Physical or sexual abuse (past and/or present)
- Peer norms in favor of drug use
- Misperception and/or power of age group peer norms
- Conflicts, such as dependence versus independence, adult maturational tasks versus fear, low self-esteem, etc.

Major Risk Factors for *Adolescents*
(continued)

- Teenage risk-taking, omnipotence, or invulnerability
- Cultural definition of use as a rite of passage into adulthood
- Cultural definition of use as glamorous, fun, etc.

Major Risk Factors for *Adults*

- Disappointment when life's expectations are not met or realization of unattainable goals
- Retirement—loss of a meaningful role or occupational identity
- Boredom with daily routines
- Loss, grief, or isolation—loss of parents, divorce, death of a spouse, or departure of children

Notes

_____

_____

_____

_____

_____

_____

_____

_____

_____

_____

_____

_____

_____

_____

_____

_____

_____

_____

_____

_____

_____

_____

_____

_____

_____

_____

Biological Explanations for the Use and Abuse of Drugs

- Genetic and biophysiological theories
  - Addiction is based on genes, brain dysfunction, and biochemical patterns
  - Biological explanations emphasize the central nervous system (CNS)
- Reward centers in some people are more sensitive to drugs resulting in more pleasure and greater rewarding experiences

Three Principal Biological Theories

- Abused drugs are positive reinforcers
- Drug abuse and psychiatric disorders
- Genetic explanations

Abused Drugs as Positive Reinforcers

This explanation believes that most drugs with abuse potential _enhance the pleasure centers_ by causing the release of _dopamine_, which is a specific brain neurotransmitter.

Notes

Genetic Explanations for Contribution to Drug Abuse Vulnerability

- Character traits, such as insecurity and vulnerability, may be genetically determined
- Factors that determine how difficult it will be to break a drug addiction may be genetically determined

Psychological Explanations for the Use and Abuse of Drugs

- The American Psychiatric Association classifies severe drug dependence as a form of psychiatric disorder.
- Drugs that are abused can cause mental conditions that mimic major psychiatric illness.
- It is sometimes difficult to distinguish between psychological and substance-related problems. Psychological problems primarily deal with mental or emotional states, often associated with or exacerbated by social and environmental factors.

Psychological Explanations for the Use and Abuse of Drugs (continued)

- Psychological factors of addiction include:
  - escape from reality
  - boredom
  - inability to cope with anxiety
  - destructive self-indulgence (constantly desiring intoxicants)
  - blind compliance with drug-abusing peers
  - self-destructiveness
  - blindly using drugs without wanting to understand the harmful effects of drug use

Notes

_____

_____

_____

_____

_____

_____

_____

_____

_____

_____

_____

_____

_____

_____

_____

_____

_____

_____

_____

_____

_____

_____

_____

_____

Theories Based on Learning

- **Conditioning**—the close association of significant reinforcing stimulus with another less significant or neutral stimulus
- **Habituation**—repeating certain patterns of behavior until they become established or habitual
- **"Addiction to pleasure" theory**—assumes it is biologically normal to continue a pleasure stimulus when once begun

Who Is at Risk?

- People at the highest risk of drug use and addiction are known as **drug sensation-seeking individuals or sensation-seekers.**
  - These individuals continually search for new or novel thrills in their experiences, and are known to have a relentless desire to pursue physical and psychological stimulation often involving dangerous behavior.
  - Usually these types of individuals also maintain a constant preoccupation with getting high.

Social Psychological Learning Theories

- If the effects of drug use become personally rewarding, "or becomes reinforcing through conditioning, the chances of continuing to use are greater than stopping"
- Differential reinforcement

Notes

Sociological Explanations

- Social Influence theories—focus on microscopic explanations that concentrate on the roles played by significant others and their impact on the individual.
- Structural influence theories—focus on macroscopic explanations of drug use and the assumption that the organizational structure of society has a major impact on individual drug use.

Sociological Explanations (continued)

- Social influence theories—focus on microscopic explanations that concentrate on the roles played by significant others and their impact on the individual.
- Structural influence theories—focus on macroscopic explanations of drug use and the assumption that the organizational structure of society has a major impact on individual drug use.

Social Influence Theories

- Social learning theory explains drug use as a form of learned behavior.
- Social influence and the role of significant others says the use of drugs is learned during intimate interaction with others who while using the drug serve as a primary group.

Notes

_____

_____

_____

_____

_____

_____

_____

_____

_____

_____

_____

_____

_____

_____

_____

_____

_____

_____

_____

_____

_____

_____

Social Influence Theories (continued)

- **Labeling theory** says people whose opinions we value have a determining influence over our self-image.
- **Subculture theory** explains that peer pressure is at the origin of drug experimentation, use, and/or abuse.

Structural Influence Theories

- **Structural influence theories**—focus on how the _organization_ of a society, group, or subculture is largely responsible for drug abuse by its members
- **Social disorganization and social strain theories**—drug use is caused by rapid and disruptive social change in society
- **Control theories**—believe that if people are left without bonds to other groups (family, peers, social institutions), they have a tendency to deviate from expected cultural values, norms, and attitudes
  - Socialization: internal and external controls

Danger Signals of Drug Abuse

- Do those close to you often ask about your drug use? Have they noticed changes in your moods or behavior?
- Are you defensive if a friend or relative mentions your drug or alcohol use?
- Are you sometimes embarrassed or frightened by your behavior under the influence of drugs or alcohol?

Notes

Danger Signals of Drug Abuse (continued)

- Have you ever gone to see a new doctor because your regular physician would not prescribe the drug you wanted?
- When you are under pressure or feel anxious, do you automatically take a depressant, stimulant, or drink?
- Do you take drugs more often or for purposes other than those recommended by your doctor?

Danger Signals of Drug Abuse (continued)

- Do you mix drugs and alcohol?
- Do you drink or take drugs regularly to help you sleep?
- Do you have to take drugs to relieve boredom or get through the day?
- Do you think you have a drug problem?

Low-Risk and High-Risk Drug Choices

- **Low-risk drug choices** refer to values and attitudes that lead to controlling the use of alcohol or drugs—self-monitoring your drug use behavior and abstinence.
- **High-risk drug choices** refer to developing values and attitudes that lead to using drugs both habitually and addictively—constantly searching for drinking and drug parties, hanging with drug abusers, etc.

CHAPTER 3

Drug Use, Regulation, and the Law

The chapter outline provides you with an organizational guide to the topics and ideas presented in this chapter of the text.

◎ Key Terms

Define the following terms:

1. Thalidomide _____

2. Switching policy _____

3. Supply reduction _____

4. Inoculation _____

5. Drug courts _____

6. Pragmatic drug policy _____

◎ Fill-in-the-Blank

1. The _____ required manufacturers to indicate the amounts of alcohol, morphine, opium, cocaine, heroin, and marijuana extract on the label of each product.

2. _____ is a birth defect hat involves impaired development of the arms, legs, or both.

3. The first legitimate effort by the U.S. government to regulate addicting substances was the _____ _____.

4. _____ involves attempts to decrease individuals' tendencies to use drugs with emphasis on reformulating values and behaviors.

5. The policy of cutting off or destroying supplies of illicit drugs is called _____ _____.

6. If _____ were approved, marijuana would become legal, while other drugs such as heroin and cocaine would remain illegal.

◎ Identify

1. Identify society's two major guidelines for controlling drug development and marketing.

   a. _____

   b. _____

   c. _____

2. The Durham-Humphrey Amendment to the Food, Drug, and Cosmetic Act established criteria for determining whether a drug should be classified as prescription or nonprescription. Identify the three categories that determine if a drug is considered nonprescription.

   a. _____

   b. _____

   c. _____

3. Identify and explain the three regulatory steps for new prescription drugs.

   a. _____

   b. _____

   c. _____

4. Identify the criteria that must be satisfied if a drug is to be switched to OTC status?

a. _____

b. _____

c. _____

◎ Discussion Questions

1. Name and explain an example of a law or an amendment that has been passed to allow an exception to FDA new prescription drug regulations. Explain why the regulation is important. _____

_____

_____

2. Discuss the effects of advertising on the drug industry. _____

_____

_____

3. Why are drug laws not always a satisfactory deterrent against the use of illicit drugs? _____

_____

_____

4. Discuss the drug legalization debate. What are the arguments being presented for and against the legalization of drugs? What are some possible compromises? What do you think is the best option?

_____

_____

5. Discuss the pros and cons of drug testing. _____

_____

_____

Notes

_____

_____

_____

_____

_____

_____

_____

_____

_____

_____

_____

_____

_____

_____

_____

_____

_____

_____

_____

_____

_____

_____

_____

_____

_____

NINTH EDITION

Glen R. Hanson
Peter J. Venturelli
Annette E. Fleckenstein

Drugs and Society

Drug Use, Regulation, and the Law

Chapter 3

Guidelines for Controlling Drug
Development and Marketing

- Society has the right to protect itself from
  the damaging impact of drug use.
- Society has the right to demand safe and
  effective drugs.

Patent Medicines

- The patent medicines of the late 1800s and
  early 1900s demonstrated to the public the
  problems of insufficient regulation of the
  drug industry.

Notes

Patent Medicines (continued)

- Early patent medicines were sometimes:
  - Ineffective
  - Addictive
  - Harmful

The 1906 Pure Food and Drug Act

- Required manufacturers to include on labels the amounts of alcohol, morphine, opium, cocaine, heroin, or marijuana extract in each product
- Marked the beginning of involvement by the government in drug manufacturing and promotion
- Did not prohibit distribution of dangerous preparations

The Sherley Amendment in 1912

- Manufacturers' therapeutic claims were not controlled by the Pure Food and Drug Act.
- The Sherley Amendment in 1912 was passed to strengthen existing law and required that labels should not contain "any statement...regarding the curative or therapeutic effect...which is false and fraudulent."

Notes

_____

_____

_____

_____

_____

_____

_____

_____

_____

_____

_____

_____

_____

_____

_____

_____

_____

_____

_____

_____

_____

_____

_____

_____

Federal Food, Drug and Cosmetic Act

- All nonnarcotic drugs were available OTC prior to World War II.
- Drug safety was not covered in existing law.
- The sale and use of Elixir Sulfanilamide led to a tragic accident that killed over 100 people.

Food, Drug, and Cosmetic Act (continued)

- Defined drugs to include products that affect bodily structure or function even in the absence of disease.
- Allowed the manufacturer to determine whether drug was to be labeled prescription or nonprescription.

Durham-Humphrey Amendment

- Made formal distinction between prescription and nonprescription drugs
- Established drug classification categories
  - Drug is habit forming
  - Drug is not safe for self-medication
  - Drug is a new drug and not shown to be completely safe

Notes

Kefauver-Harris Amendment

- Consequence of thalidomide tragedy
- Drug manufacturers had to demonstrate the efficacy and safety of drugs
- The FDA was empowered to withdraw approval of a drug that was already being marketed
- The FDA regulated and evaluated drug testing by pharmaceutical companies

Regulating New Drug Development

- The amended Food, Drug, and Cosmetic Act requires that all new drugs be registered with and approved by the FDA.

Regulating New Drug Development (continued)

- The FDA is mandated by Congress to:
  - Ensure the rights and safety of human subjects during clinical testing
  - Evaluate the safety and efficacy of new treatments
  - Compare benefits and risks of new drugs and determine approval

Notes

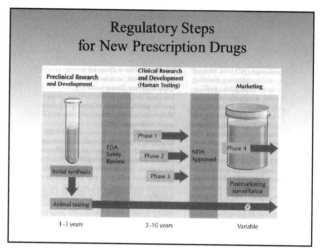

Regulatory Steps for New Prescription Drugs (continued)

- Step 1. Preclinical research and development
- Step 2. Clinical research and development
  - Initial clinical stage
  - Clinical pharmacological evaluation stage
  - Extended clinical evaluation
- Step 3. Permission to market
  - Postmarketing surveillance

Exceptions: Special Drug-Marketing Laws

- "Fast-track" rule
  - Applied to testing of certain drugs for rare cancers, AZT for the treatment of AIDS, etc.
- Orphan Drug Law
  - Tax advantages for development of drugs to treat "rare diseases" since this can be otherwise unprofitable
- Prescription Drug User Fee Act of 1992
  - Increase reviewers and decrease review time

Notes

The Regulation of Nonprescription Drugs

- In 1972, the FDA initiated a program to evaluate the effectiveness and safety of nonprescription drugs
- The FDA evaluated each active ingredient in OTC medications and placed ingredients into three categories:
  - Safe and effective
  - Not safe and effective or unacceptable indications
  - Insufficient data to permit final classification

Switching Policy

- The drug must have been used by prescription for 3 years.
- Use must have been relatively high during the time it was used by prescription.
- Adverse drug reactions must not be alarming, and the frequency of side effects must not have increased during the time the drug was available to the public.

Prescription Advertising

- Many pharmaceutical companies advertise medications directly to the public.
  - Concerns that consumers will put pressure on physicians to prescribe inappropriately due to these ads
- A large amount of drug promotion is directed at health professionals and controlled by the FDA.

Notes

_____

_____

_____

_____

_____

_____

_____

_____

_____

_____

_____

_____

_____

_____

_____

_____

_____

_____

_____

_____

_____

_____

_____

_____

_____

_____

The Harrison Act of 1914

- First federal legislation to regulate and control the production, importation, sale, purchase, and free distribution of opium or drugs derived from opium

The Comprehensive Drug Abuse Prevention and Control Act of 1970

- This act divided substances with abuse potential into categories based on the degree of their abuse potential and clinical usefulness
- Schedules I, II, III, IV, V

"Scheduling"

- Schedule I substances have high-abuse potential and no currently approved medicinal uses; they cannot be prescribed.
- Schedule II substances have high-abuse potential but are approved for medical uses and can be prescribed.
- Schedule I–V reflects the likelihood of abuse and clinical usefulness.

Notes

Drug Laws and Deterrence

- The increase in illegal drug use and drug addiction that began in the 1960s forced society to evaluate its view of drugs.

Drug Laws and Deterrence (continued)

- If a person abuses a drug, should he or she be treated as a criminal or as a sick person inflicted with a disease?

Drug Laws and Deterrence (continued)

- How is the user (supposedly the victim) distinguished from the pusher (supposedly the criminal) of an illicit drug, and who should be more harshly punished?

Notes

_____

_____

_____

_____

_____

_____

_____

_____

_____

_____

_____

_____

_____

_____

_____

_____

_____

_____

_____

_____

_____

_____

_____

Drug Laws and Deterrence (continued)

- Are the laws and associated penalties effective deterrents against drug use or abuse, and how is effectiveness determined?

Strategies for Preventing Drug Abuse

- Supply reduction
  - Using drug laws to control the manufacturing and distribution of classified drugs
- Inoculation
  - Aims to protect drug users by teaching them responsibility and explaining the effects of drugs on bodily and mental functioning
- Demand reduction strategy
  - Aims to reduce the actual demand for drugs

Suggestions for Reducing Demand

- A top priority of prevention is to reduce demand by youth.
- Education must be carefully designed for the target population.
- Attitudes toward drug abuse must be changed.
- Replacement therapy can be useful.

Notes

Drug Courts

• Designed to deal with nonviolent, drug-abusing offenders

• Integrate mandatory drug testing, substance abuse treatment, sanctions, and incentives in a judicially supervised setting

• Provide support to rebuild lives

• Have had a positive impact

Drug Legalization Debate

• Violence and crime would decrease/increase?
• Profits associated with illegal trade would decrease/increase?
• Law enforcement costs would decrease/increase?
• Addiction would decrease/increase?
• Societal/health costs would decrease/increase?
• Consumption would increase/decrease?

Areas of Compromise?

• Selective legalization?
• Control through prescription or special outlets?
• Discretionary enforcement of drug laws?

Notes

Drug Testing

- In response to the demand by society to stop the spread of drug abuse and its adverse consequences, drug testing has been implemented in some situations to detect drug users.

Drug Testing (continued)

Common types of drug testing include:
- Breathalyzers
- Urine, blood, and hair specimens

Pragmatic Drug Policies

- The government must develop programs that are consistent with the desires of the majority of the population.
- Programs must de-emphasize interdiction and stress programs that reduce demand.

Notes

Pragmatic Drug Policies (continued)

- Government and society must better understand how laws, used properly and selectively, can reinforce and communicate expected social behavior and values.
- Programs such as antismoking campaigns should be implemented that employ "public consensus" more effectively.

CHAPTER 4

Homeostatic Systems and Drugs

The chapter outline provides you with an organizational guide to the topics and ideas presented in this chapter of the text.

◎ Key Terms

Define the following terms:

1. Homeostasis _____

2. Neurons _____

3. Axon _____

4. Receptors _____

5. Synapse _____

6. Endorphins _____

7. Hormones _____

8. Anabolic steroids _____

◎ Fill-in-the-Blank

1. Chemical messengers released by neurons are called _____.

2. Drugs that affect mood or alter the state of consciousness are _____

   _____.

3. _____ are chemical messengers released into the blood by glands.

4. A _____ is a minute gap between a neuron and target cell,

   across which neurotransmitters travel.

5. _____ are short branches of neurons that receive transmitter signals.

6. Receptors activated by opioid narcotic drugs such as heroin and morphine are called _____

   _____.

7. A drug may have two different effects on a receptor when interaction occurs: _____

   _____ or _____.

8. Agents that mimic the effects of norepinephrine or epinephrine are _____

   _____.

9. Male sex hormones are called _____.

◎ Identify

1. Identify and describe three neurotransmitters.

   a. _____

   b. _____

   c. _____

2. Identify three brain regions that are influenced by drugs of abuse and describe characteristics of each.

   a. _____

   _____

   b. _____

   _____

   c. _____

   _____

◎ Discussion Questions

1. Describe the process of sending messages by neurons. _____

_____

_____

_____

2. Why are many athletes (and some nonathletes) attracted to androgens? What are the hormones' positive and negative side effects? Do you think that classifying anabolic steroids as Schedule III drugs is justified? _____

_____

_____

_____

Notes

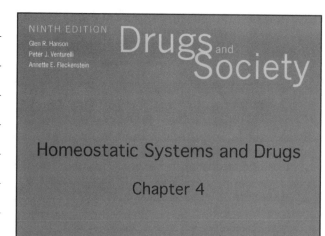

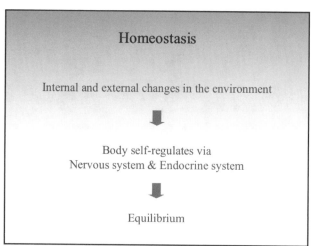

Notes

Transfer of Messages by Neurons

- The receiving region of the neuron is affected by a chemical message that either excites or inhibits it.
- Excitatory message
  - impulse moves from the receiving region of the neuron down the axon to the sending region (*terminal*)
  - chemical messengers (*neurotransmitters*) are released

Transfer of Messages by Neurons
(continued)

- Neurotransmitters travel and attach to receiving proteins called *receptors* on target cells
- Activation of receptors causes a change in the activity of the target cell; the target cells can be other neurons or cells that make up organs, muscles, or glands

---

Sending Messages by Neurons

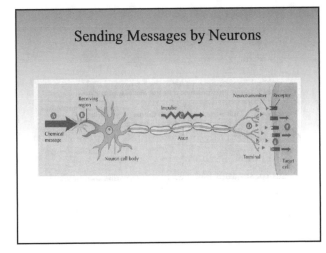

Notes

_____

_____

_____

_____

_____

_____

_____

_____

_____

_____

_____

_____

_____

_____

_____

_____

_____

_____

_____

_____

_____

_____

Neurons

- Neurons can send discrete excitatory or inhibitory messages to their target cells.
- Neurons are distinguished by the type of neurotransmitter they release.
- Neurotransmitters represent a wide variety of chemical substances and functions.
  - Example: Dopamine activates the pleasure center.

Common Neurotransmitters

Neurotransmitter	type of effect	CNS changes	drugs of abuse
Dopamine	inhibitory-excitatory	euphoria agitation paranoia	amphetamines, cocaine
GABA	inhibitory	sedation relaxation drowsiness depression	alcohol, Valium-type barbiturates
Serotonin	inhibitory	sleep relaxation sedation	LSD
Acetylcholine	excitatory-inhibitory	mild euphoria excitation insomnia	tobacco, nicotine
Endorphins	inhibitory	mild euphoria block pain slow respiration	narcotics

Neurons (continued)

- *Dendrites*—the receiving regions of a neuron's cell body
- Each neuron in the central nervous system is in close proximity with other neurons
- Although they are close, neurons never actually touch

Notes

Neurons (continued)

- *Synapse*—the point of communication between one neuron and another

- *Synaptic cleft*—the gap between neurons at the synapse

Synapses

- *Excitatory synapse*—initiates an impulse in the receiving neuron when stimulated, causing release of neurotransmitters or increasing activity in target cell
- *Inhibitory synapse*—diminishes likelihood of an impulse in the receiving neuron or reduces the activity in other target cells

Synapses (continued)

- A receiving neuron or target cell may have many synapses
- Final cellular activity is a *summation* of these many excitatory and inhibitory synaptic signals

Notes

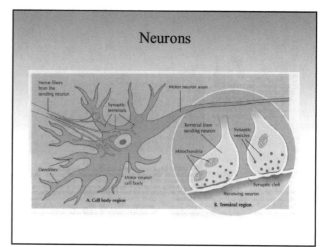

Neurons

Neurons

Drug Receptors

- The chemical messengers from glands and neurons exert their effects by interacting with special protein regions in membranes called *receptors*.
- Receptors only interact with molecules that have specific configurations.

Drug Receptors

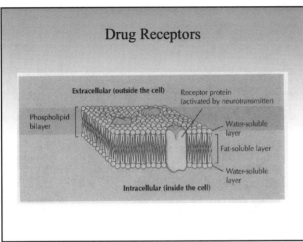

Drug Receptors (continued)

- *Agonists*—substances or drugs that activate receptors

- *Antagonists*—substances or drugs that attach to receptors and prevent them from being activated

Drug Receptors

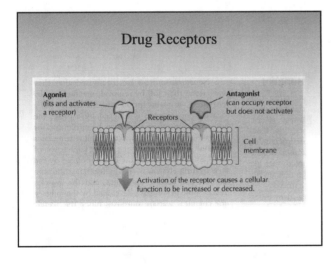

Notes

Notes

_____

_____

_____

_____

_____

_____

_____

_____

_____

_____

_____

_____

_____

_____

_____

_____

_____

_____

_____

_____

_____

_____

_____

Neurotransmitters

- Many drugs affect the activity of neurotransmitters by altering their synthesis, storage, release, or deactivation.
- Neurotransmitters frequently altered by drugs of abuse:
  - Acetylcholine
  - Catecholamines
  - Serotonin
  - GABA
  - Endorphins

Major Divisions of the Nervous System

- Two major components of the nervous system
  - Central nervous system (CNS)
  - Peripheral nervous system (PNS)

Central Nervous System

- CNS
  - Brain
  - Spinal cord
- CNS receives information from PNS, evaluates information, then regulates muscle and organ activity via PNS

Notes

Peripheral Nervous System

- Consists of input and output nerves
- Input to brain and spinal cord
  - Conveys sensory info (pain, pressure, temperature)
- Output—two types
  - Somatic (control of voluntary muscles)
  - Autonomic (control of unconscious functions)

Central Nervous System

- Reticular activating system
  - Receives input from all the sensory systems and cerebral cortex
  - Controls the brain's state of arousal (sleep vs. awake)
- Basal ganglia
  - Controls motor activity
- Limbic system
  - Regulates emotional activities, memory, and endocrine activity
  - Dopamine

Central Nervous System (continued)

- The cerebral cortex
  - Helps interpret, process, and respond to information
- The hypothalamus
  - Controls endocrine and basic body functions

Notes

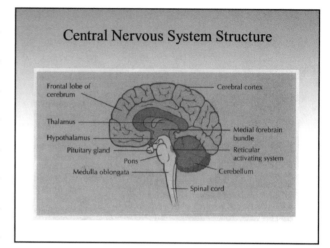

Central Nervous System Structure

Frontal lobe of cerebrum

Cerebral cortex

Thalamus

Hypothalamus

Medial forebrain bundle

Pituitary gland

Reticular activating system

Pons

Medulla oblongata

Cerebellum

Spinal cord

Autonomic Nervous System

- Sympathetic and parasympathetic system
  - These systems work in an antagonistic fashion to control unconscious, visceral functions such as breathing and cardiovascular activity
- Sympathetic system
  - Norepinephrine
- Parasympathetic system
  - Acetylcholine

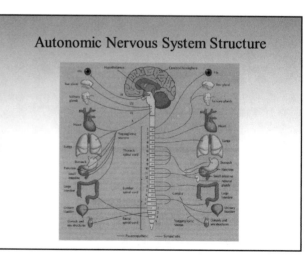

Autonomic Nervous System Structure

Notes

Introduction to the Endocrine System

- The endocrine system consists of secreting glands (e.g., adrenal, thyroid, pituitary)
- These glands produce substances called hormones (e.g., adrenaline, steroids, insulin, and sex hormones)
- These substances are information transferring molecules

Introduction to the Endocrine System
(continued)

- Hormones are secreted into the bloodstream and carried by the blood to all the organs and tissues of the body.
- Hormones affect selected tissues that are designed to receive the information.
- Hormones may be highly selective or very general with regard to the cells or organs they influence.

Introduction to the Endocrine System

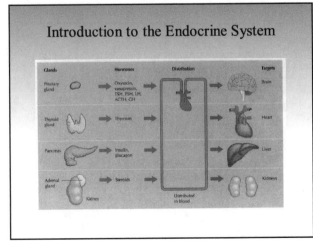

Notes

_____

_____

_____

_____

_____

_____

_____

_____

_____

_____

_____

_____

_____

_____

_____

_____

_____

_____

_____

_____

_____

_____

_____

_____

_____

_____

_____

_____

_____

_____

The Abuse of Hormones: Anabolic Steroids

- Androgens
  - Produce growth of muscle mass
  - Increase body weight
- Anabolic steroids
  - Are structurally related to the male hormone testosterone
  - Sometimes abused by athletes and body builders to improve strength and appearances

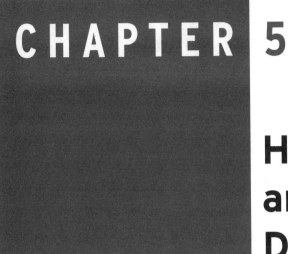

CHAPTER 5

How and Why Drugs Work

The chapter outline provides you with an organizational guide to the topics and ideas presented in this chapter of the text.

◎ Key Terms

Define the following terms:

1. Side effects _____

2. Withdrawal _____

3. Tolerance _____

4. Threshold dose _____

5. Half-life _____

6. Reverse tolerance _____

7. Cross-tolerance _____

8. Mental set _____

9. Placebo effect _____

10. Dysphoric _____

◎ Fill-in-the-Blank

1. The correlation between the amount of a drug given and its effects is _____

_____.

2. _____ occurs when the presence of one drug alters the action of another drug.

3. The _____ is selective filtering between the cerebral blood vessels and

the brain.

4. The maximum drug effect, regardless of dose, is the _____.

5. The _____ is the buildup of a drug in the body after

multiple doses taken at short intervals.

6. The process of changing the chemical properties of a drug, usually by metabolism, is called _____

_____.

7. Chemical products of metabolism are called _____.

8. Something that causes physical defects in the fetus is said to have _____

properties.

9. Paradoxical effects that occur when a drug has been eliminated from the body are called _____

_____.

10. _____ occurs when dependence on a drug can

be relieved by other similar drugs.

◎ Identify

1. Identify five pharmacokinetic issues that should be considered when attempting to anticipate a drug's
effects.

a._____

b._____

c._____

d. _____

e. _____

2. Identify and describe four methods of taking drugs.

a. _____

b. _____

c. _____

d. _____

3. Identify three ways injection may be administered.

a. _____

b. _____

c. _____

4. Identify four possible side effects that can result from drug use.

a. _____

b. _____

c. _____

d. _____

5. Identify four factors that affect a drug's distribution.

a. _____

b. _____

c. _____

d. _____

◎ Matching

Match the drug interaction with its description:

___ Additive interactions

___ Potentiation

___ Synergism

___ Antagonistic interactions

a. effects created when drugs cancel one another out

b. ability of one drug to enhance the effect of another

c. effects created when drugs are similar and actions are added together

◎ Discussion Questions

1. Discuss the difference between potency and toxicity. What factors determine a drug's potency? _____

_____

_____

_____

2. Why is it is important for people to be aware of drug interactions? _____

_____

_____

_____

3. Discuss the importance of time as a factor in the body's response to a drug. _____

_____

_____

_____

4. Discuss how drug effects can be modified by factors such as age, gender, and pregnancy. Why is it important for those with diseases to be especially careful when taking drugs? _____

_____

_____

_____

5. Discuss psychological dependence. How does it develop? What are its effects? How does psychological dependence to such things as tobacco and caffeine-containing beverages differ from dependence to other substances? _____

_____

_____

_____

6. What is your mental set? What factors in your life contribute to your view of drugs?_____

_____

_____

_____

7. What factors do you think most influence the risk of drug abuse for an individual? Many are mentioned in the text. Can you think of any others? _____

_____

_____

Notes

_____

_____

_____

_____

_____

_____

_____

_____

_____

_____

_____

_____

_____

_____

_____

_____

_____

_____

_____

_____

_____

_____

_____

_____

NINTH EDITION

Glen R. Hanson
Peter J. Venturelli
Annette E. Fleckenstein

Drugs and **Society**

How and Why Drugs Work

Chapter 5

Intended and Unintended Effects of Drugs

- Intended responses
  - reason for using the drug
- Unintended responses
  - side effects
- The main distinction between intended responses and side effects depends on the therapeutic objective

Common Side Effects of Drugs

- Nausea or vomiting
- Changes in mental alertness
- Dependence
  - Withdrawal
- Allergic reactions
- Changes in cardiovascular activity

Notes

_____

_____

_____

_____

_____

_____

_____

_____

_____

_____

_____

_____

_____

_____

_____

_____

_____

_____

_____

_____

_____

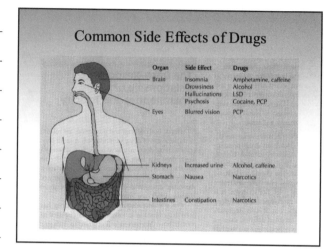

Common Side Effects of Drugs

Organ	Side Effect	Drugs
Brain	Insomnia	Amphetamine, caffeine
	Drowsiness	Alcohol
	Hallucinations	LSD
	Psychosis	Cocaine, PCP
Eyes	Blurred vision	PCP
Kidneys	Increased urine	Alcohol, caffeine
Stomach	Nausea	Narcotics
Intestines	Constipation	Narcotics

Adverse Effects of Drugs

- Q. Approximately how many people in the United States die each year because of adverse side effects of prescription and nonprescription drugs?
- A. 100,000

Dose-Response

- Many factors can affect the way an individual responds to a drug, including the following:
  - Dose
  - Tolerance
  - Potency

Notes

Dose-Response (continued)

- Additional factors
  - Pharmacokinetic properties
    - Rate of absorption
    - Manner distributed throughout the body
    - Rate metabolized and eliminated
  - Form of the drug
  - Manner in which the drug is administrated

Dose-response Curve

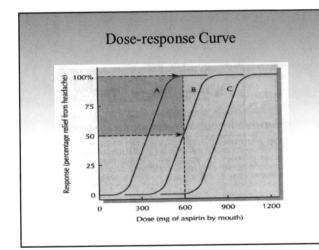

Dose-response Curve

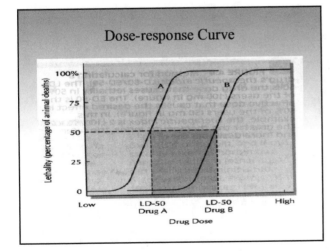

Notes

_____

_____

_____

_____

_____

_____

_____

_____

_____

_____

_____

_____

_____

_____

_____

_____

_____

_____

_____

_____

_____

_____

_____

Margin of Safety

- The range in dose between the amount of drug necessary to cause a therapeutic effect and a toxic effect

---

Potency vs. Toxicity

Potency

the amount of drug necessary to cause an effect

Toxicity

the capacity of a drug to do damage or cause adverse effects in the body

---

Drug Interaction

- Additive effects
  - Summation of effects of drugs taken concurrently
- Antagonistic (inhibitory) effects
  - One drug cancels or blocks effects of another
- Potentiative (synergistic) effects
  - Effect of a drug is enhanced by another drug or substance

Notes

Pharmacokinetic Factors That Influence Drug Effects

- Administration
- Absorption
- Distribution
- Activation
- Biotransformation and elimination

Forms and methods of taking drugs

- oral ingestion
- inhalation
- injection
- topical application

Distribution

- Most drugs are distributed throughout the body in the blood
- It takes approximately 1 minute for a drug to circulate throughout the body after it enters the bloodstream
- Drugs have different patterns of distribution depending on their chemical properties

Notes

_____

_____

_____

_____

_____

_____

_____

_____

_____

_____

_____

_____

_____

_____

_____

_____

_____

_____

_____

_____

_____

_____

Required doses for effects

- **Threshold dose** – the minimum amount of a drug necessary to have an effect
- **Plateau effect** – the maximum effect a drug can have regardless of the dose
- **Cumulative effect** – the buildup of drug concentration in the body due to multiple doses taken within short intervals

Time-Response Factors

- The closer a drug is placed to the target area, the faster the onset of action.
- Acute drug response
  - Immediate or short-term effects after a single drug dose
- Chronic drug response
  - Long-term effects after a single dose

Biotransformation

- **Biotransformation**—the process of changing the chemical or pharmacological properties of a drug by metabolism
- The liver is the major organ that metabolizes drugs in the body
- The kidney is the next most important organ for drug elimination

Notes

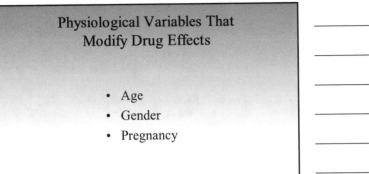

Physiological Variables That
Modify Drug Effects

- Age
- Gender
- Pregnancy

Adaptive Processes

- **Tolerance** – changes causing decreased response to a set dose of a drug
- **Dependence** – the physiological and psychological changes or adaptations that occur in response to the frequent administration of a drug
- **Withdrawal**

Adaptive Processes

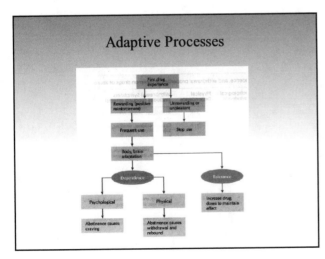

Notes

_____
_____
_____
_____
_____
_____
_____
_____
_____
_____
_____
_____
_____
_____
_____
_____
_____
_____
_____
_____
_____
_____
_____

Tolerance

- Reverse tolerance (sensitization)
  - Enhanced response to a given drug dose; opposite of tolerance
- Cross-tolerance
  - Development of tolerance to one drug causes tolerance to related drugs

Drug Dependence

Physical dependence

Psychological dependence

Psychological factors affecting drug effect

- Individual's mental set
- Placebo effects

Notes

Addiction and Abuse

- The term *addiction* has many meanings. It is often used interchangeably with dependence, either physiological or psychological in nature; other times, it is used synonymously with the term drug abuse.

Addiction and Abuse

- Factors affecting variability in dependence
  - Hereditary factors
  - Drug craving

Addiction and Abuse

- Other factors contributing to drug use patterns
  - Positive versus negative effects of drug
  - Peer pressure
  - Home, school, work environment
  - Mental state

CHAPTER 6

CNS Depressants: Sedative-Hypnotics

The chapter outline provides you with an organizational guide to the topics and ideas presented in this chapter of the text.

Introduction
An Introduction to CNS Depressants
    The History of CNS Depressants
    The Effects of CNS Depressants: Benefits and Risks

Types of CNS Depressants
    Benzodiazepines: Valium-Type Drugs
    Barbiturates
    Other CNS Depressants
Patterns of Abuse with CNS Depressants
    Treatment for Withdrawal

◎ Key Terms

Define the following terms:

1. Barbiturates _____

2. Antihistamines _____

3. Anxiolytic _____

4. Amnesiac _____

5. Paradoxical effects _____

6. Detoxification _____

◎ Fill-in-the-Blank

1. The most popular and safest CNS depressants in use today are _____

    _____.

2. _____ are CNS depressants used to relieve anxiety, fear, and apprehension.

3. CNS depressants used to induce drowsiness and encourage sleep are _____

    _____.

4. _____ is used to achieve a controlled state of unconsciousness so that a patient can be treated, usually by surgery, in relative comfort and without memory of an unpleasant experience.

5. The restive phase of sleep associated with dreaming is called _____ _____.

6. A drug used at all-night raves, parties, dance clubs, and bars to enhance sensory experiences is called a _____.

◎ Identify

1. Why are CNS depressants problematic? Give four reasons.

   a._____

   b._____

   c._____

   d._____

2. Identify four medical uses of benzodiazepines.

   a._____

   b._____

   c._____

   d._____

3. What are some common side effects of benzodiazepines? _____

   _____

   _____

   _____

4. Identify three ways that benzodiazepines are abused.

   a._____

   b._____

   c._____

5. Identify and briefly describe three other kinds of CNS depressants (CNS depressants other than barbiturates and benzodiazepines).

   a._____

   b._____

   c._____

◎ True/False

Tell whether each statement is true or false. If false, explain why the statement is incorrect.

1. All CNS depressants are created equal._____

_____

2. Benzodiazepines are primarily distinguished by their duration of action._____

_____

3. Antihistamines produce the same responses in all people. _____

_____

◎ Discussion Questions

1. What is GABA? How do benzodiazepines affect GABA?_____

_____

_____

_____

2. What are some negative effects of benzodiazepines such as Halcion and Xanax? Do you think the FDA made the right decision when it allowed Halcion to stay on the market despite court rulings and critic complaints? _____

_____

_____

_____

3. Why are benzodiazepines preferred over barbiturates? What are the effects of uncontrolled use of barbiturates? _____

_____

_____

_____

4. What types of people are most likely to abuse CNS depressants? What are some ways in which these people use CNS depressants? _____

_____

_____

5. How does one treat withdrawal? What are some of the dangers associated with treating individuals who are severely dependent on CNS depressants? _____

_____

_____

_____

Notes

_____

_____

_____

_____

_____

_____

_____

_____

NINTH EDITION **Drugs**and**Society**
Glen R. Hanson
Peter J. Venturelli
Annette E. Fleckenstein

CNS Depressants: Sedative-Hypnotics

Chapter 6

_____

_____

_____

_____

_____

_____

_____

_____

Introduction to CNS Depressants

- Why are CNS depressants problematic?
  - Usually prescribed under physician direction
  - Can cause very alarming and dangerous behavior if not closely monitored
    - Most problems associated with these drugs due to inadequate professional supervision

_____

_____

_____

_____

_____

_____

_____

_____

_____

Introduction to CNS Depressants

- Why are CNS depressants problematic? (continued)
  - Seemingly unrelated drug groups can cause CNS depression
    - Combination use can cause dangerous drug interactions
  - Can cause disruptive personality changes

Notes

The History of CNS Depressants

- Attempts to find CNS depressants other than alcohol began in the 1800s
- Bromides were introduced to treat nervousness and anxiety in the 1800s
  - Very popular but toxic
- In the early 1900s, bromides were replaced by barbiturates
  - Initially heralded as safe and effective
  - But problems with tolerance, dependence, and safety

The History of CNS Depressants
(continued)

- In the 1950s the first benzodiazepines were marketed as substitutes for barbiturates
  - Relatively safe when used for short periods
  - Long-term use can cause dependence and withdrawal problems

---

The History of CNS Depressants
(continued)

- Benzodiazepines were routinely prescribed for stress, anxiety, or apprehension
  - In 1973 100 million prescriptions were written for benzodiazepines
  - Twice as many women as men taking them
  - "Mother's Little Helper" by the Rolling Stones
- As medical community became aware of the problem, use of depressants declined

Notes

The Effects of CNS Depressants

- CNS depressants reduce CNS activity and diminish the brain's level of awareness
- Depressant drugs include:
  - Benzodiazepines
  - Barbiturate-like drugs
  - Alcohol
  - Antihistamines
  - Opioid narcotics like heroin

The Effects of CNS Depressants
(continued)

- Depressants are usually classified according to the degree of their medical effects on the body. For example:
  - *Sedatives* cause mild depression and relaxation
    - *Anxiolytic*—drugs that relieve anxiety
  - *Hypnotics* induce drowsiness and encourage sleep
    - *Amnesiac* effects can cause the loss of memory

The Effects of CNS Depressants
(continued)

- The same drug can cause different effects based on dose
  - Low dose (sedatives—relieve anxiety and promote relaxation)
  - Higher doses (hypnotics—can cause drowsiness and promote sleep)
  - Even higher doses (anesthetics—can cause anesthesia and are used for patient management during surgery)

Notes

_____

_____

_____

_____

_____

_____

_____

_____

_____

_____

_____

_____

_____

_____

_____

_____

_____

_____

_____

_____

_____

_____

_____

_____

Types of CNS Depressants

Benzodiazepines: Valium-Type Drugs
- Prescribed for anxiety and sleep
- 4 of the 40 top-selling prescription drugs in the U.S. in 2003
- Medical uses
  - Relief from anxiety, treatment of neurosis, relaxation of muscles, alleviation of lower-back pain, treatment of convulsive disorders, induction of sleep, relief from withdrawal symptoms, induction of amnesia

Types of CNS Depressants
(continued)

- Mechanisms of action for benzodiazepine
  - Affect neurons that have receptors for the neurotransmitter GABA
- GABA—inhibitory transmitter in brain regions
  - Limbic system (alter mood)
  - RAS (cause drowsiness)
  - Motor cortex (relax muscles)

Types of CNS Depressants
(continued)

- Types of benzodiazepines
  - 14 benzodiazepine compounds available in the U.S.
  - Distinguished primarily by their duration of action: short-acting (hypnotics), long-acting (sedatives)
- Side effects
  - Drowsiness to paradoxical effects
  - Tolerance, dependence, withdrawal, and abuse

Notes

Types of CNS Depressants
(continued)

- **Barbiturates** played an important role as sedative-hypnotic agents
- However, due to their narrow margin of safety and their abuse liability, they were replaced by benzodiazepines
  - Caused many negative side effects from nausea to death from respiratory or cardiovascular depression

---

Other Types of CNS Depressants

- Drugs with barbiturate-like properties
  - Chloral hydrate
  - Glutethimide
  - Methyprylon
  - Methaqualone
- Antihistamines
- GHB (gamma hydroxybutyrate)

Patterns of Abuse
with CNS Depressants

- The American Psychiatric Association considers dependence on CNS depressants a psychiatric disorder

Notes

Patterns of Abuse
with CNS Depressants (continued)

- People most likely to abuse CNS depressants include individuals who
  - Use drugs to relieve continual stress
  - Paradoxically feel euphoria and stimulation from depressants
  - Use depressants to counteract the unpleasant effects of other drugs of abuse
  - Combine depressants with alcohol and heroin to potentiate the effects

Patterns of Abuse
with CNS Depressants (continued)

- *Detoxification*—the elimination of a toxic substance, such as a drug, and its effects
  - With CNS depressants, this is achieved by substituting a longer-acting barbiturate for the offending CNS depressant and gradually reducing the dose

CHAPTER 7

Alcohol: Pharmacological Effects

The chapter outline provides you with an organizational guide to the topics and ideas presented in this chapter of the text.

◎ Key Terms

Define the following terms:

1. Fermentation _____

2. Mead _____

3. Ethanol _____

4. Social lubricant _____

5. Blood alcohol concentration (BAC) _____

6. Behavioral tolerance _____

7. Hepatotoxic effect _____

8. Cirrhosis _____

9. Alcoholic cardiomyopathy_____

◎ Fill-in-the-Blank

1. The process of heating fermented mixtures of cereal grains or fruits in a still to evaporate and be

   trapped as purified alcohol is called _____.

2. A drug that blocks sensitivity to pain is an _____.

3. The principal enzyme that metabolizes ethanol is _____

   _____.

4. The concurrent use of multiple drugs is called _____.

5. _____ is the loss of conditioned reflexes due to depression of

   inhibitory centers of the brain.

6. A drug or substance that increases the production of urine is a _____.

7. _____ is a psychotic condition connected with heavy

   alcohol use and associated vitamin deficiencies.

◎ Identify

1. Identify four negative consequences of drinking alcohol.

   a._____

   b._____

   c._____

   d. _____

2. Identify four factors that determine how alcohol will affect an individual's body.

   a._____

   b._____

   c._____

   d. _____

3. Identify and describe the three prototypic stages of withdrawal.

   a._____

   b._____

   c._____

4. Describe the three phases of alcohol-induced liver disease.

a._____

b._____

c._____

5. Describe how alcohol consumption affects each of the following:

a. Digestive system _____

_____

b. Blood_____

_____

c. Cardiovascular system _____

_____

d. Sexual organs_____

_____

e. Endocrine system_____

_____

f. Kidneys _____

_____

g. Brain _____

_____

h. Fetus _____

_____

_____

◎ Matching

Match the type of alcohol with its description.

_____ Methyl alcohol

_____ Ethylene glycol

_____ Isopropyl alcohol

_____ Ethyl alcohol

a. Rubbing alcohol

b. Alcohol used in beverages

c. Wood alcohol

d. Alcohol used as antifreeze

◎ True/False

Tell whether each statement is true or false. If false, explain why the statement is incorrect.

1. Alcohol is the most widely used and abused psychoactive drug. _____

_____

2. It is estimated that at some time during their lives, almost 50% of all Americans will be involved in an

alcohol-related traffic accident. _____

_____

3. Drinking black coffee or taking a cold shower will hasten the sobering process. _____

_____

◎ Discussion Questions

1. Why is alcohol perceived as acceptable for social use as well as for relieving stress and anxiety? Why do

many people often forget alcohol's harmful consequences? _____

_____

_____

_____

2. What are some possible reasons why people use alcohol with other drugs, like marijuana?_____

_____

_____

_____

3. What is meant by "taking the hair of the dog that bit you"? Is this an effective method of reducing

hangovers? Why or why not?_____

_____

_____

_____

Notes

_____

_____

_____

_____

_____

_____

_____

_____

_____

_____

_____

_____

_____

_____

_____

_____

_____

_____

_____

_____

_____

_____

_____

_____

_____

_____

_____

NINTH EDITION

Drugs and **Society**

Glen R. Hanson
Peter J. Venturelli
Annette E. Fleckenstein

Alcohol:
Pharmacological Effects

Chapter 7

Alcohol as a Drug

- Alcohol is a psychoactive drug that is a CNS depressant
- Alcohol is the second most widely used and abused of all psychoactive drugs
- Q. What drug is the *most* widely used and abused drug?
- A. Caffeine

Alcohol as a Drug
(continued)

- Alcohol is an addictive drug
- Social psychologists refer to the perception of alcohol as a social lubricant
- Four reasons why many people view alcohol as a non-drug
  - Alcohol is legal
  - Advertising and media promote drinking as normal
  - Large distribution and sales of alcohol
  - Long history of alcohol use

Notes

_____

_____

_____

_____

_____

_____

_____

_____

_____

_____

_____

_____

_____

_____

_____

_____

_____

_____

_____

_____

_____

_____

Negative Impact of Alcohol

- 100,000 deaths associated with alcohol each year
- Nearly 50% of all Americans will be involved in an alcohol-related traffic accident sometime during their lives

Negative Impact of Alcohol
(continued)

- Alcohol causes severe dependence
- Disrupts personal, family, social, and professional functioning
- Illness, accidents, violence, and crime related to alcohol use

Negative Impact of Alcohol
(continued)

- Fetal alcohol syndrome
- Alcohol is the second leading cause of premature death in America
- Approximately $167 billion are spent annually dealing with social and health problems related to alcohol use

Notes

Four types of alcohol

- Methyl alcohol – poisonous

- Isopropyl alcohol – poisonous

- Ethylene glycol – poisonous

- Ethanol – drinking alcohol

Physical Effects of Alcohol

- The body is affected by alcohol in two ways:
  - Direct contact in mouth, esophagus, stomach, and intestine
  - Influence on almost every organ system in the body after entering the bloodstream
- Absorption is the process by which the drug molecules reach the bloodstream
- The effects of alcohol on the human body depend on the amount of alcohol in the blood (BAC)

Physical Effects of Alcohol
(continued)

- BAC produced depends on
  - Presence of food in the stomach
  - Rate of alcohol consumption
  - Concentration of alcohol
  - Drinker's body composition
- Alcoholic beverages have no vitamins, minerals, protein, or fat—just a large amount of carbohydrates and usually calories

Notes

Physical Effects of Alcohol
(continued)

- Alcohol can cause severe physical and psychological dependence
  - *Cross-tolerance*
  - *Behavioral tolerance*—compensation of motor impairments through behavioral pattern modification by chronic alcohol users

Blood Alcohol Concentration (BAC)

- Almost 95% of consumed alcohol is inactivated by liver metabolism.
- The liver metabolizes alcohol at a slow and constant rate and is unaffected by the amount ingested.
- Thus, if one can of beer is consumed each hour, the BAC will remain constant.

How Alcohol Is Absorbed in the Body

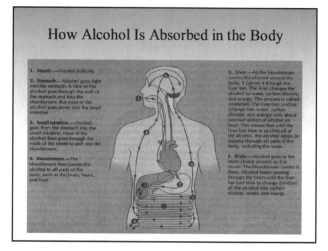

Notes

Polydrug Use

- It is common practice to take alcohol concurrently with other drugs (*polydrug use*)

Polydrug Use
(continued)

- Reasons why individuals may combine alcohol with other drugs
  - Alcohol enhances properties of other CNS depressants
  - Decreases the amount of an expensive and difficult-to-get drug required to achieve the desired effect
  - Helps diminishes side effects of other drugs
  - There is a common predisposition to use alcohol and other drugs

Short-term Effects of Alcohol

- Low to moderate doses
  - Disinhibition
  - Social setting and mental state may determine individual response
    - Euphoric, friendly, talkative
    - Aggressive and hostile
  - Interfere with motor activity, reflexes, and coordination

Notes

_____

_____

_____

_____

_____

_____

_____

_____

_____

_____

_____

_____

_____

_____

_____

_____

_____

_____

_____

_____

_____

_____

Short-term Effects of Alcohol (continued)

- Moderate quantities
  - Slightly increases heart rate
  - Slightly dilates blood vessels in arms, legs, skin
  - Moderately lowers blood pressure
  - Stimulates appetite
  - Increases production of gastric secretions
  - Increases urine output

Short-term Effects of Alcohol (continued)

- At higher doses
  - Social setting has little influence on effects
  - Difficulty in walking, talking, and thinking
  - Induces drowsiness and causes sleep

Short-term Effects of Alcohol (continued)

- Large amounts consumed rapidly
  - Severe depression of the brain system and motor control area of the brain
    - Uncoordination, confusion, & disorientation
    - Stupor, anesthesia, coma, or death
- Lethal level of alcohol is between 0.4 and 0.6% by volume in the blood

Notes

True or False

- Drinking black coffee, taking a cold shower, or breathing pure oxygen will hasten the sobering up process?
- The type of alcohol beverage you drink can influence the hangover that results?
- Taking an aspirin-caffeine combination after drinking helps the sobering up process and the chances of having a hangover?

Principal Control Centers of the Brain Affected by Alcohol

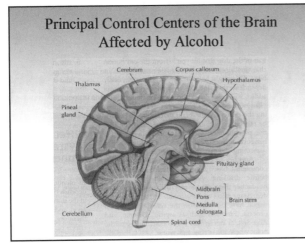

Effects of Alcohol on Organ Systems and Bodily Functions

- Brain and nervous system
- Liver
    - Hepatotoxic effect
    - Alcoholic hepatitis
    - Cirrhosis
- Digestive system

Notes

_____

_____

_____

_____

_____

_____

_____

_____

_____

_____

_____

_____

_____

_____

_____

_____

_____

_____

_____

_____

_____

_____

_____

_____

_____

_____

_____

_____

_____

_____

Effects of Alcohol on Organ Systems and Bodily Functions (continued)

- Blood
- Cardiovascular system
  - Alcoholic cardiomyopathy
- Sexual organs
- Endocrine system

Effects of Alcohol on Organ Systems and Bodily Functions (continued)

- Kidneys
- Mental disorder and damage to the brain
  - Wernicke-Korsakoff's syndrome
- The fetus
  - Fetal alcohol syndrome (FAS)

Alcohol and Pregnancy

- Moderate to excessive drinking during pregnancy can result in
  - Spontaneous abortion
  - Damage to fetus
    - Fetal alcohol syndrome (FAS)
      - Damage dose-related
      - A safe lower level of alcohol consumption has not been established for pregnant women

Other Effects of Alcohol on Organ Systems and Bodily Functions

- Gender differences
- Malnutrition

Notes

_____

_____

_____

_____

_____

_____

_____

_____

_____

_____

_____

_____

_____

_____

_____

_____

_____

_____

_____

_____

_____

_____

_____

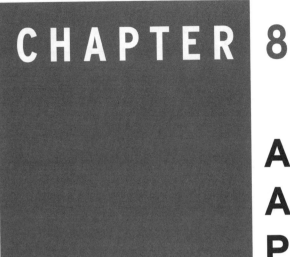

CHAPTER 8

Alcohol: A Behavioral Perspective

The chapter outline provides you with an organizational guide to the topics and ideas presented in this chapter of the text.

◎ Key Terms

Define the following terms:

1. Binge drinking _____

2. Teetotalers _____

3. Bootlegging _____

4. Drunken comportment _____

5. Pseudointoxicated _____

6. Relapsing syndrome _____

7. Acute alcohol withdrawal syndrome _____

_____

8. Delirium tremens _____

9. Psychodrama _____

10. Post-traumatic stress disorder _____

_____

◎ Fill-in-the-Blank

1. People who drink five or more alcoholic beverages on one occasion for five or more days within any given 10-day period are _____.

2. Places where alcoholic beverages were illegally sold during the Prohibition area were called _____ _____.

3. The ingredients in _____ were secret, often consisting of large amounts of colored water, alcohol, cocaine, or opiates.

4. _____ is uncontrollable drinking that leads to alcohol craving, loss of control, and physical dependence but with less prominent characteristics than found in _____ _____, which is a state of physical and psychological addiction to ethanol.

5. A _____ is a psychoactive chemical that depresses thought and judgment functions in the cerebral cortex, which has the effect of allowing relatively unrestrained behavior.

6. _____ refers to the individual's expectation of what a drug will do to his or her personality; _____ is the physical and social environments where the drug is consumed.

7. Unplanned and unwanted forced sexual attack from a friend or date partner is known as _____ _____.

8. _____ is a therapeutic technique in which group members play assigned parts to elicit emotional reactions.

9. A family therapy technique that records information about behavior and relationships on a type of family tree to elucidate persistent patterns of dysfunctional behavior is a _____ _____.

◎ Identify

1. Identify three major developments that occurred as a result of Prohibition.

a._____

b._____

c._____

2. Identify and define four major components of alcoholism.

a._____

b._____

c._____

d._____

3. Identify and describe Jellinek's six categories of alcoholism.

a._____

_____

b._____

_____

c._____

_____

e._____

_____

f._____

_____

g._____

_____

4. Identify three reasons why women respond differently than men to alcohol.

a._____

b._____

c._____

5. Identify two ways family members give destructive support to alcohol addicts. Explain and give an example of each.

a._____

_____

b._____

_____

6. Identify three ways in which the treatment of alcoholism differs from the treatment of other drug addictions.

a._____

b._____

c._____

◎ Discussion Questions

1. A large percentage of those who drink alcohol are below the legal drinking age or 21. Do you think the drinking age should be lowered? Why or why not? _____

_____

_____

_____

2. What is the cost of alcohol abuse on society? Give multiple examples. _____

_____

_____

_____

3. How did the slave trade contribute to colonial America's alcohol production? _____

_____

_____

_____

4. Why is it difficult to establish one universal definition of alcoholism? _____

_____

_____

_____

5. How does one's culture influence behavior regarding the use and abuse of alcohol?_____

_____

_____

_____

6. How do cultures other than America view drinking? Discuss a different culture and the ways in which that culture approaches alcohol. _____

_____

_____

_____

7. Why are alcohol use and binge drinking so prevalent on college campuses? _____

_____

_____

_____

8. In what ways does alcoholism affect one's entire family? How does the family react and adapt to having an alcoholic member? What help is available to the family of an alcoholic? _____

_____

_____

_____

Notes

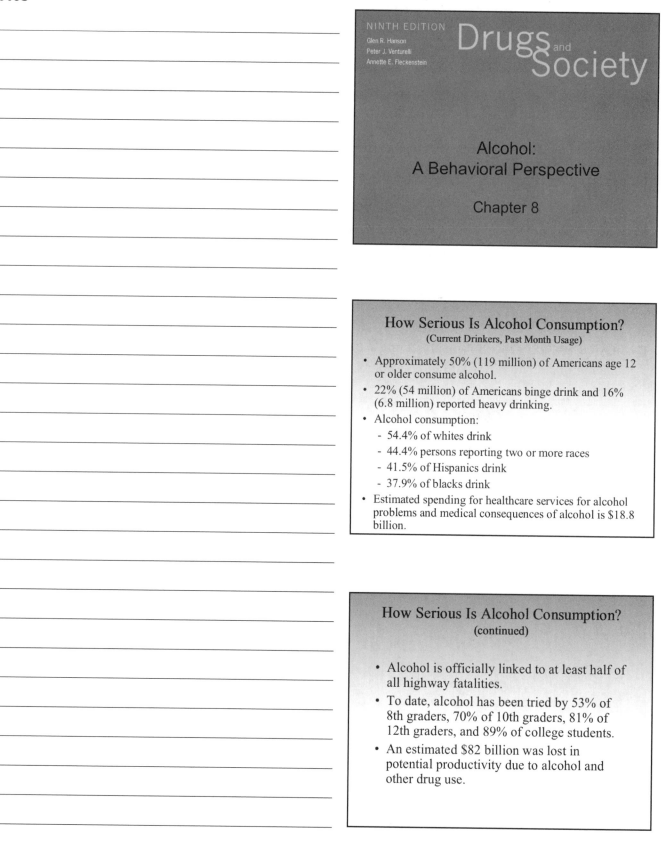

NINTH EDITION
Glen R. Hanson
Peter J. Venturelli
Annette E. Fleckenstein

Drugs and Society

Alcohol:
A Behavioral Perspective

Chapter 8

How Serious Is Alcohol Consumption?
(Current Drinkers, Past Month Usage)

- Approximately 50% (119 million) of Americans age 12 or older consume alcohol.
- 22% (54 million) of Americans binge drink and 16% (6.8 million) reported heavy drinking.
- Alcohol consumption:
  - 54.4% of whites drink
  - 44.4% persons reporting two or more races
  - 41.5% of Hispanics drink
  - 37.9% of blacks drink
- Estimated spending for healthcare services for alcohol problems and medical consequences of alcohol is $18.8 billion.

How Serious Is Alcohol Consumption?
(continued)

- Alcohol is officially linked to at least half of all highway fatalities.
- To date, alcohol has been tried by 53% of 8th graders, 70% of 10th graders, 81% of 12th graders, and 89% of college students.
- An estimated $82 billion was lost in potential productivity due to alcohol and other drug use.

Notes

How Serious Is Alcohol Consumption?
(continued)

Driving Under the Influence of Alcohol:
- An estimated 13.6 % of persons aged 12 or older drove under the influence of alcohol (DUI).
  - 9.7% of 16- or 17- year-olds
  - 20.1% of 18- to 20- year-olds
  - 28.7% of 21- to 25- year-olds
  - Beyond 25, these rates declined with increasing age
- Males were nearly twice as likely as females (18.2% versus 9.3%) to drive under the influence of alcohol.

History of Alcohol (Ethanol) in America

- 1830 was the peak drinking period
- Prohibition period

Alcohol Has Coincided with Major Historical Events:
- Colonial America
- Triangle trade (New England Yankees traded rum for slaves in Africa, then slaves for molasses in West Indies, then back to New England to make rum)
- Colonial taverns (a key institution?)

History of Alcohol (Ethanol) in America
(continued)

- Temperance movement (1830–1850)
- Prohibition era (1920–1933)
  - Ratification of the Eighteenth Amendment (1919)
  - Alcohol was outlawed (January 1920)
    - Speakeasies
    - Bootlegging
    - Patent medicines
- In 1933 the 21st Amendment repealed prohibition

Notes

_____

_____

_____

_____

_____

_____

_____

_____

_____

_____

_____

_____

_____

_____

_____

_____

_____

_____

_____

_____

_____

_____

Major Developments Resulting from Prohibition

1. Alcohol use began to diminish for the first 2 or 3 years after Prohibition was in effect. However, after 3 years of steady decline, the use of distilled liquors rose every year afterward.
2. Enforcement against alcohol use was overthrown by corruption in law enforcement.
3. The early European Immigrants strongly populating American cities during Prohibition, came from cultures that viewed drinking as normal, resulting in their refusal to give up alcohol consumption.

Defining Alcoholism

- There is no agreement regarding at what specific point someone is an alcoholic.
- Alcoholism is a state of physical and psychological addiction to a psychoactive substance known as ethanol.
- Most definitions include chronic behavioral disorders, repeated drinking to the point of loss of control, health disorders, and difficulty functioning socially and economically.

Defining Alcoholism
(first definition)

World Health Organization (WHO) definition:
- *"Alcohol dependence syndrome* is characterized by a state, psychic and usually also physical, resulting from drinking alcohol. This state is characterized by behavioral and other responses that include a compulsion to take alcohol on a continuous or periodic basis to experience its psychic effects and sometimes to avoid the discomfort of its absence; tolerance may or may not be present" (NIAAA, 1980).

Notes

Defining Alcoholism
(second definition)

- "Alcoholism is a chronic behavioral disorder manifested by repeated drinking of alcoholic beverages in excess of the dietary and social uses of the community, and to an extent that interferes with the drinker's health or his social or economic functioning" (Keller, 1958/78).

Defining Alcoholism
(third definition)

- "Alcoholism is a chronic, primary, hereditary disease that progresses from an early, physiological susceptibility into an addiction characterized by tolerance changes, physiological dependence, and loss of control over drinking. Psychological symptoms are secondary to the physiological disease and not relevant to its onset'' (Gold 1991, 99).

Major Known Components of Alcoholism

–Craving

–Very impaired or loss of control

–Physical dependence

–Increasing tolerance

Notes

_____

_____

_____

_____

_____

_____

_____

_____

_____

_____

_____

_____

_____

_____

_____

_____

_____

_____

_____

_____

_____

_____

_____

_____

_____

_____

_____

Types of Alcoholics

- Alpha alcoholics
- Beta alcoholics
- Gamma alcoholics
- Delta alcoholics
- Epsilon alcoholics
- Zeta alcoholics

Culture and Alcohol

- **Drunken comportment** is behavior exhibited while under the direct influence of alcohol determined by the norms and expectations of a particular culture.
- **Disinhibitor** is a psychoactive chemical that depresses thought and judgment functions in the cerebral cortex, which has the effect of allowing relatively unrestrained behavior (as in alcohol inebriation).

Cultural Considerations

- Some psychologists contend that both *set and setting* can overshadow the pharmacological effects of most drugs, including alcohol.

    Set—an individual's expectation of what a drug will do to his/her personality

    Setting—the physical and social environment where most drugs, including alcohol, are consumed

Notes

Culture and Alcohol

- Cultural rules state how much one can drink, and where.
- Cultures provide ceremonial meaning to alcohol use.
  - Drinking rates among Jews
  - Drinking rates among Irish
- Culture provides a model of alcoholism.
- Attitudes regarding drinking in the U.S.

Cultural Considerations

- Some sociologists contend that a culture's views and attitudes can influence effects of alcohol
  - Abstinent cultures (strictly prohibit alcohol)
  - Ambivalent cultures (contradictory views)
  - Permissive cultures (promote alcohol)
  - Over-permissive cultures (encourage alcohol)
- Which type or types of alcohol culture(s) does the U.S. have?

Alcohol Abuse Among College and University Students

- CORE Institute research results:
  - 300,000 of the nation's 12 million college students will die of alcohol-related causes such as drunk-driving accidents, liver disorders, sexually transmitted diseases, cancers from alcohol abuse, and severely damaged organs from chronic drinking.
  - College students consume an average of 4.3 drinks per week.
  - Male students at smaller institutions consumed far more than those at larger institutions.

Notes

_____

_____

_____

_____

_____

_____

_____

_____

_____

_____

_____

_____

_____

_____

_____

_____

_____

_____

_____

_____

_____

_____

_____

_____

_____

Alcohol Abuse Among College and University Students (continued)

Other studies found that
- 42–50% of college students binge drink.
- Males binge drink more than females.
- For binge drinkers, the impact on impaired academic performance is just as great for women drinkers.
- Being white, involved in athletics, or a resident of a fraternity or sorority made it more likely that a student would be a binge drinker.

Alcohol Abuse Among College and University Students (continued)

- On American campuses, alcohol is a factor in 40% of all academic problems and 28% of all dropouts.
- 75% of male students and 55% of female students involved in acquaintance rape had been drinking or using drugs.
- The transition into college is associated with a doubling of the percentages of those who drink for both genders.
- With heavier drinkers, grades suffered for both male and female students.

Women and Alcohol

- Women possess greater sensitivity to alcohol, have a greater likelihood of addiction, and develop alcohol-related health problems sooner than men.
- More women in alcohol treatment come from sexually abusive homes (70%), in comparison to men (12%).

Notes

Three Major Reasons Why Women Are More Sensitive to the Effects of Alcohol

- Body size (men generally larger than women)
- Women absorb alcohol sooner—women possess more body fat and body fat does not dilute alcohol
- Women possess less of a metabolizing enzyme—this enzyme gets rid of (processes out) alcohol

Alcohol Consumption Patterns of Women

- Women 21 to 34 years of age were least likely to report alcohol-related problems if they had stable marriages and were working full time.
- Between 35 to 49 years of age, the heaviest drinkers were divorced or separated women without children.
- Between 50 to 64 years of age, the heaviest drinkers were women whose husbands/partners drank heavily.
- Women 65 and older comprised less than 10% of drinkers with drinking problems.

Alcohol Consumption in the U.S.

- Alcohol consumption has dropped sharply since 1981.
- What explains the steady decline in alcohol consumption?
  - Demographics
  - Conservatism
  - Decrease in social acceptability
  - Increased awareness of risks
  - Increased concerns for health

Notes

_____
_____
_____
_____
_____
_____
_____
_____
_____
_____
_____
_____
_____
_____
_____
_____
_____
_____
_____
_____
_____
_____
_____
_____

Additional Facts Regarding Alcohol Use/Abuse

- Drinking and Driving—On most weekend nights throughout the United States, 70% of all fatal single-vehicle crashes involve a driver who is legally intoxicated.
- Income/Wealth—Less affluent people drink less than more affluent individuals.
- The Average "Alcoholic"—Most alcoholics are secret or disguised drinkers who look very much like common working people.
- On Average—Most people who consume alcohol do not become problem drinkers.

Alcohol and the Family

- **Co-dependency** or *co-alcoholism* is a relationship pattern in which addicted or nonaddicted family members identify with the alcohol addict and deny the existence of alcohol consumption as a problem.
- **Enabling** is denial or making up of excuses for the excessive drinking of an alcohol addict to whom someone is close.

Alcohol and the Family (continued)

- Organizations for victims of alcoholics
  - Children of Alcoholics (COAs) 2–4 times more likely to become alcoholics themselves
  - Adult Children of Alcoholics (ACOAs) 2–4 times more likely to develop alcoholism
- It is estimated that there are 28.6 million COAs in the U.S. and 6.6 million are under the age of 18
- COAs and ACOAs are more likely to marry into families where alcoholism is prevalent
- 25% of American children are exposed to an alcoholic before the age of 18

Notes

Helping the Family Recover

- **Psychodrama** is a family therapy in which significant inter- and intra-personal issues are enacted in a focused setting using dramatic techniques.
- **Genogram** is a family therapy technique that records information about behavior and relationships on a type of family tree to elucidate persistent patterns of dysfunctional behavior.
- **Role-playing** is a therapeutic technique in which group members play assigned parts to elicit emotional actors.

Helping the Family

- **Post-traumatic stress disorder** is a psychiatric syndrome in which an individual who has been exposed to a traumatic event or situation experiences psychological stress that may manifest itself in a wide range of symptoms, including re-experiencing the trauma, numbing of general responsiveness, and hyper-arousal.

Recovery from Alcoholism

- Treatment of alcoholism
  - Denial as a psychological defense
  - Easy to relapse without radical shift in lifestyle
  - Alcohol rehabilitation and medical ramifications
  - More emotionally fragile than other addicts
  - *Relapsing syndrome*

Notes

_____

_____

_____

_____

_____

_____

_____

_____

_____

_____

_____

_____

_____

_____

_____

_____

_____

_____

_____

_____

_____

_____

Withdrawal

- **Relapsing syndrome** refers to returning to the use of alcohol after quitting.
- **Acute alcohol withdrawal syndrome** refers to symptoms that occur when an alcohol addicted individual does not maintain his/her usual blood alcohol level.
- **Delirium tremens** is the most severe, even life-threatening form of alcohol withdrawal, involving hallucinations, deliriums, and fever.

CHAPTER 9

Narcotics (Opioids)

The chapter outline provides you with an organizational guide to the topics and ideas presented in this chapter of the text.

◎ Key Terms

Define the following terms:

1. Analgesics _____

2. Speedballing _____

◎ Fill-in-the-Blank

1. _____ are drugs that are derived from opium.

2. Drugs that block coughing are _____.

3. To _____ is to inject a drug of abuse intravenously.

◎ Identify

1. Identify three therapeutic uses for narcotics.

a._____

b._____

c._____

2. What are some possible side effects of opioid narcotics? _____

_____

_____

_____

3. Identify and describe the two major stages in the development of a psychological dependence on heroin or other opioid narcotics.

a._____

b._____

4. Identify six goals of heroin dependency treatment.

a._____

b._____

c._____

d._____

e._____

f._____

◎ Matching

Match the drug with its description.

____ Morphine

____ Methadone

____ Fentanyls

____ Hydromorphone

____ Oxycodone (Oxycontin)

____ Meperidine

____ Buprenorphine

____ Codeine

____ Pentazocine

____ Propoxyphene

____ Dextromethorphan

____ Clonidine

____ Naloxone/Naltrexone

a. prepared from morphine and used as an analgesic and cough suppressant.

b. stimlulates receptors for noradrenaline; used to relieve some physical effects of opiate withdrawal; nonaddictive.

c. effective in relieving the cravings for narcotic pain relievers with minimal tendency to cause addiction itself.

d. often substituted for heroin in the treatment of narcotic-dependent people.

e. synthetic used in cough remedies; no analgesic action.

f. will precipitate withdrawal symptoms if given to a person on methadone. maintenance; not commonly abused because its effects can be unpleasant, resulting in dysphoria.

g. relatively pure narcotic antagonists; prevent narcotic drugs from having an effect.

h. much weaker analgesic; in very high doses, it can cause delusions, hallucinations, and convulsions.

i. commonly used to relieve moderate to intense pain that cannot be controlled by less potent and less dangerous narcotics.

j. considered to be an important and effective therapy for the treatment of severe pain from cancer or other lingering diseases.

k. very potent narcotic analgesics that are often administered intravenously for general anesthesia.

l. naturally occurring constituent of opium; most frequently prescribed of the narcotic analgesics.

m. synthetic drug frequently used for treatment of moderate pain; repeated high doses can cause seizures.

◎ Discussion Questions

1. Discuss ways to treat heroin dependency. What are mistakes some people make when trying to treat this? _____

_____

_____

_____

2. Why does heroin addiction often contribute to criminal activity? _____

_____

_____

_____

Notes

_____

_____

_____

_____

_____

_____

_____

_____

_____

_____

_____

_____

_____

_____

_____

_____

_____

_____

_____

_____

_____

_____

_____

_____

_____

NINTH EDITION

Glen R. Hanson
Peter J. Venturelli
Annette E. Fleckenstein

Drugs and Society

Narcotics (Opioids)

Chapter 9

What Are Narcotics?

- The term *narcotic* currently refers to naturally occurring substances derived from the opium poppy and their synthetic substitutes.
- These drugs are referred to as the opioid (or opiate) narcotics because of their association with opium.

What Are Narcotics? (continued)

- The opioid narcotics possess abuse potential, but they also have important clinical value (analgesic, antitussive).
- The term *narcotic* has been used to label many substances, from opium to marijuana to cocaine.

Notes

_____
_____
_____
_____
_____
_____
_____
_____
_____
_____
_____
_____
_____
_____
_____
_____
_____
_____
_____

The History of Narcotics

- A 6,000-year-old Sumerian tablet
- The Egyptians
- The Greeks
- Arab traders
- China and opium trade
- The Opium War of 1839
- American opium use

The History of Narcotics (continued)

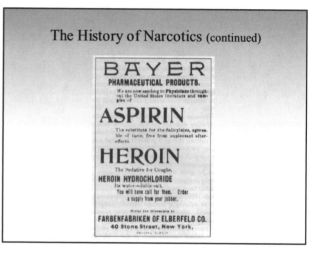

Pharmacological Effects

- The most common clinical use of the opioid narcotics is as analgesics to relieve pain.
- The opioid narcotics relieve pain by activating the same group of receptors that are controlled by the endogenous substances called *endorphins*.
- Activation of opioid receptors blocks the transmission of pain through the spinal cord or brain stem.

Notes

Pharmacological Effects
(continued)

- *Morphine* is a particularly potent pain reliever and often is used as the analgesic standard by which other narcotics are compared.
- With continual use, tolerance develops to the analgesic effects of morphine and other narcotics.
- Physicians frequently underprescribe narcotics, for fear of causing narcotic addiction.

Pharmacological Effects
(continued)

- The principal side effects of the opioid narcotics, besides their abuse potential, include:
  - Drowsiness, mental clouding
  - Respiratory depression
  - Nausea, vomiting, and constipation
  - Inability to urinate
  - Drop in blood pressure

Abuse, Tolerance, Dependence, and Withdrawal

- All the opioid narcotic agents that activate opioid receptors have abuse potential and are classified as scheduled drugs.
- Tolerance begins with the first dose of a narcotic, but does not become clinically evident until after 2 to 3 weeks of frequent use.

Notes

_____

_____

_____

_____

_____

_____

_____

_____

_____

_____

_____

_____

_____

_____

_____

_____

_____

_____

_____

_____

_____

_____

_____

_____

_____

Abuse of Opioid Narcotics

- Tolerance occurs most rapidly with high doses given in short intervals.
- Doses can be increased as much as 35 times in order to regain the narcotic effect.
- Physical dependence invariably accompanies severe tolerance.
- Psychological dependence can also develop with continual narcotic use.

Heroin Abuse

- Heroin is classified as a Schedule I drug.
- Heroin is one of the most widely abused illegal drugs in the world.
- Heroin was illicitly used more than any other drug of abuse in the U.S. (except for marijuana) until 20 years ago, when it was replaced by what drug?
  -Cocaine

Heroin Combinations

- Pure heroin is a white powder.
- Heroin is usually "cut" (diluted) with **lactose**.
- When heroin first enters the U.S., it may be 95% pure; by the time it is sold, it may be 3% to 60% pure.
- If users are unaware of the variance in purity and do not adjust doses accordingly, results can be fatal.

Notes

Heroin Combinations
(continued)

- Heroin has a bitter taste and is often cut with **quinine**, which can be a deadly adulterant.
- Heroin plus the artificial narcotic **fentanyl** can be dangerous due to its unexpected potency.
- Heroin is most frequently used with **alcohol**.
- Heroin combined with **cocaine** is called "speedballing."

Facts About Heroin Abuse

- Q. How many deaths occur annually in the United States from heroin overdoses?
- A. Approximately 3,000 to 4,000 deaths
- Q. What is the estimated number of heroin addicts in the United States?
- A. 600,000
- Q. What are "shooting galleries"?
- A. Locations that serve as gathering places for addicts

Heroin and Crime

- Factors related to crime
  - Pharmacological effects encourage antisocial behavior that is crime-related
  - Heroin diminishes inhibition
  - Addicts are self-centered, impulsive, and governed by need
  - Cost of addiction
  - Similar personality of criminal and addict

Notes

_____

_____

_____

_____

_____

_____

_____

_____

_____

_____

_____

_____

_____

_____

_____

_____

_____

_____

_____

_____

_____

_____

_____

Patterns of Heroin Abuse

- Heroin use among adolescents and young adults declined slightly in 2001 and 2002
- Heroin has become purer (60% to 70% purity) and cheaper
- Greater purity leads users to administer heroin in less efficient ways
- Many youth believe that heroin can be used safely if not injected

Patterns of Heroin Abuse
(continued)

- Because of its association with popular fashions and entertainment, heroin has been viewed as glamorous and chic, especially by many young people, although lately this attitude has been changing.
- Emergency room visits due to narcotic overdoses have increased significantly since 1990.

Stages of Dependence

- Initially, the effects of heroin are often unpleasant.
- Euphoria gradually overcomes the aversive effects.
- The positive feelings increase with narcotic use, leading to psychological dependence.

Notes

Stages of Dependence (continued)

- After psychological dependence, physical dependence occurs with daily use over a 2-week period.
- If the user stops taking the drug after physical dependence has developed, severe withdrawal symptoms result.

Methods of Administration

- Sniffing the powder
- Injecting it into a muscle (intramuscular)
- Smoking
- Mainlining (intravenous injection)

Heroin Addicts and AIDS

- Over 50% of IV heroin users have been exposed to the AIDS virus
- Fear of contracting HIV from IV heroin use has contributed to the increase in smoking or snorting heroin
- Many who start by smoking or snorting progress to IV administration due to its more intense effects

Notes

_____

_____

_____

_____

_____

_____

_____

_____

_____

_____

_____

_____

_____

_____

_____

_____

_____

_____

_____

_____

_____

_____

_____

Heroin and Pregnancy

- Heroin use by a pregnant woman leads to
  - Physical dependence on heroin in the newborn
  - Withdrawal symptoms after birth in the newborn

Withdrawal Symptoms

- After the effects of the heroin wear off, the addicts have only a few hours in which to find the next dose before severe withdrawal symptoms begin
- A single "shot" of heroin lasts 4 to 6 hours
- Withdrawal symptoms—runny nose, tears, minor stomach cramps, loss of appetite, vomiting, diarrhea, abdominal cramps, chills, fever, aching bones, muscle spasms

Treatment

- Methadone or buprenorphine are frequently used to help narcotic addicts
- These drugs block withdrawal symptoms
- Treatment should also include regular counseling and other supplemental services such as job training

Other Narcotics

- Morphine
- Methadone
- Fentanyl
- Hydromorphone
- Oxycodone (OxyContin)
- Meperidine
- Buprenorphine
- MPTP
- Codeine
- Pentazocine
- Propoxyphene

Narcotic-Related Drugs

- **Dextromethorphan** (OTC antitussive)

- **Clonidine** (relieves some of the opioid withdrawal symptoms)

- **Naloxone/Naltrexone** (narcotic antagonist; used for narcotic overdoses)

Notes

CHAPTER 10

Stimulants

The chapter outline provides you with an organizational guide to the topics and ideas presented in this chapter of the text.

Introduction
Major Stimulants
    Amphetamines
    Cocaine
    Current Attitudes and Patterns of Abuse

Minor Stimulants
    Caffeinelike Drugs (Xanthines)
    OTC Sympathomimetics
    Herbal Stimulants

◎ Key Terms

Define the following terms:

1. Uppers _____

2. Behavioral stereotypy _____

3. Narcolepsy _____

4. Speed _____

5. Rush _____

6. High _____

7. Run _____

8. Hyperpyrexia _____

9. Freebasing _____

10. Crack babies _____

11. Xanthines _____

12. Caffeinism _____

◎ Fill-in-the-Blank

1. _____ are substances that cause the user to feel pleasant effects such as a sense of increased energy and a state of euphoria.

2. _____ are drugs that suppress one's appetite for food.

3. The two principal side effects of therapeutic doses of amphetamines are _____ and _____.

4. _____ is a smokable form of methamphetamine.

5. A _____ is similar to a run, but is usually of a shorter duration.

6. Repeated administration of methamphetamine to maintain the high is called _____ _____.

7. Combinations of amphetamine or cocaine with an opioid narcotic are called _____ _____.

8. Ecstasy is a _____, a drug used by young adults at dance parties such as raves.

9. A drug is _____ when contaminating substances are mixed in to dilute the drug.

10. Already processed and inexpensive "freebased" cocaine, ready for smoking, is called _____ _____.

◎ Identify

1. Identify and briefly discuss the three approved uses of amphetamines.

   a. _____

   b. _____

   c. _____

2. Briefly discuss the three eras of cocaine history.

a. The First Cocaine Era _____

_____

b. The Second Cocaine Era _____

_____

c. The Third Cocaine Era _____

_____

3. Identify four street names for cocaine.

a._____

b._____

c._____

d._____

4. Identify four possible effects of cocaine withdrawal.

a._____

b._____

c._____

d._____

5. Give three reasons why the combined use of cocaine and alcohol can be so dangerous.

a._____

b._____

c._____

◎ Discussion Questions

1. How were amphetamines put to use during wartime? Should they still be used today?_____

_____

_____

_____

2. How do amphetamines work in the body? _____

_____

_____

_____

3. What are some consequences of increased amphetamine use?_____

_____

_____

_____

4. How is amphetamine addiction treated? _____

_____

_____

5. Why did the early South American civilizations have fewer negative experiences with cocaine use than we do now? _____

_____

_____

_____

6. How has American cocaine use affected South American countries?_____

_____

_____

_____

7. How can cocaine be administered? How does the method of use determine the intensity of the drug's effects? _____

_____

_____

_____

8. How is cocaine addiction treated? What are the major differences in treatment approaches? How does one determine which treatment is most appropriate for an addicted individual? _____

_____

_____

_____

9. At what point does caffeine become dangerous? What effects does it have in higher doses? Should the FDA control it more tightly?_____

_____

_____

_____

Notes

_____

_____

_____

_____

_____

_____

_____

_____

_____

_____

_____

_____

_____

_____

_____

_____

_____

_____

_____

_____

_____

_____

_____

_____

_____

_____

_____

_____

NINTH EDITION

Glen R. Hanson
Peter J. Venturelli
Annette E. Fleckenstein

Drugs and Society

Stimulants

Chapter 10

Major Stimulants

- All major stimulants cause increased alertness, excitation, and euphoria; thus these drugs are referred to as "uppers."
  - Schedule I ("designer" amphetamines)
  - Schedule II (amphetamine and cocaine)

Amphetamines

- Cause dependence due to their euphoric properties and ability to eliminate fatigue
- Can be legally prescribed by physicians
- Abuse occurs in people who acquire their drugs by both legitimate and illicit ways

Notes

_____

_____

_____

_____

_____

_____

_____

_____

_____

_____

_____

_____

_____

_____

_____

_____

_____

_____

_____

_____

_____

_____

_____

_____

History of Amphetamines

- First synthesized in 1887 by L. Edeleano
- In 1927, Gordon Alles gave a firsthand account of its effects
  - Reduced fatigue
  - Increased alertness
  - Caused a sense of confident euphoria
- In 1932, Benzedrine inhalers became available as a nonprescription medication

History of Amphetamines (continued)

- The Benzedrine inhalers became widely abused for their stimulant action
  - 1971, all potent amphetamine-like compounds in nasal inhalers were withdrawn from the market
- Widely used in World War II to counteract fatigue
- Other users: Korean War soldiers, truck drivers, homemakers, high achievers under pressure
- Air Force still gives pilots low doses of amphetamine to help them maintain alertness

How Amphetamines Work

- Synthetic chemical similar to the natural neurotransmitters such as norepinephrine, dopamine, and epinephrine
- Increase the release and block the metabolism of these catecholamine substances, as well as serotonin, in the brain and nerves associated with the sympathetic nervous system

Notes

How Amphetamines Work
(continued)

- Amphetamines can cause
  - "Fight-or-flight" response
  - Alertness
  - Anxiety, severe apprehension, or panic
  - Potent effects on dopamine in the reward center of the brain
  - *Behavioral stereotypy* (meaningless repetition of a single activity)

Approved Uses of Amphetamines

Narcolepsy

Attention Deficity Hyperactivity Disorder

Weight Reduction

Side Effects of Therapeutic Doses

- Abuse
- Cardiovascular toxicities
  - Increased heart rate
  - Elevated blood pressure
  - Damage to blood vessels

Notes

_____

_____

_____

_____

_____

_____

_____

_____

_____

_____

_____

_____

_____

_____

_____

_____

_____

_____

_____

_____

_____

_____

_____

_____

Current Misuse

- Decline in abuse in the late 1880s and early 1990s
- In 1993 the declines were replaced by an increase
- Currently, 3–5% annual use of methamphetamine by adolescents in the U.S.
- Due to the ease of production, methamphetamine is often made in makeshift labs using cookbook-style recipes
- Toxic chemicals in these labs pose a threat to residents, neighbors, law enforcement officials, and the environment

Patterns of High-Dose Use

- Amphetamines can be taken
  - Orally
  - Intravenously (speed freak)
  - Smoked (ice)

Summary of the Effects of Amphetamines

	Body	Mind
low dose	increased heartbeat	decreased fatigue
	increased blood pressure	increased confidence
	decreased appetite	increased feeling of alertness
	increased breathing rate	restlessness, talkativeness
	inability to sleep	increased irritability
	sweating	fearfulness, apprehension
	dry mouth	distrust of people
	muscle twitching	behavioral stereotypy
	convulsions	hallucination
	fever	psychosis
high dose	chest pain	
	irregular heartbeat	
	death due to overdose	

Notes

Amphetamines

- Amphetamine combinations
  - Speedballs
- Designer drugs
  - Methcathinone ("CAT")
  - Methylenedioxymethamphetamine (MDMA, Ecstasy; most popular of the designer amphetamines)
  - Methylenedioxyamphetamine (MDA)
- A special amphetamine
  - Methylphenidate (Ritalin)

Cocaine

- Cocaine abuse continues to be one of the greatest drug concerns in the U.S.
- From 1978 to 1987, the U.S. experienced the largest cocaine epidemic in history.
- As recently as the early 1980s cocaine was not believed to cause dependency.
- Cocaine is known to be highly addictive.
  - In 2000, 2.7 million Americans were chronic cocaine users.

History of Cocaine

- The first cocaine era (2500 B.C.)
  - South American Indians
  - Erythroxylon coca shrub
- The second cocaine era (began 19th century)
  - Vin Mariani
  - Coca-Cola
  - Sigmund Freud
- The third cocaine era (began 1980s)
  - Celebrities
  - Decreased in price to $10 a "fix"

Notes

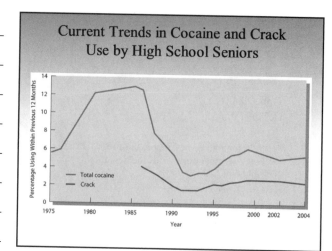

Cocaine Administration

- Form of administration important in determining intensity of cocaine's effects, its abuse liability, and likelihood of toxicity
- <u>Orally</u> (Chewing of the coca leaf)
- <u>Inhaled</u> into the nasal passages ("Snorting")
- <u>Injected</u> intravenously
- <u>Smoked</u> (Freebasing, Crack)
  - crack babies

Pharmacological Effects of Cocaine

- Enhanced activity of the catecholamine and serotonin transmitters
- Blocks the reuptake of these substances following their release from neurons
- The summation of cocaine's effects on dopamine, noradrenaline, adrenaline, and serotonin is to cause CNS stimulation
  - Cardiovascular system
  - Local anesthetic effect

Notes

3 Main Stages of Cocaine Withdrawal

- "Crash"—initial abstinence phase consisting of depression, agitation, suicidal thoughts, and fatigue
- Withdrawal—including mood swings, craving, anhedonia, and obsession with drug seeking
- Extinction—normal pleasure returns, mood swings, cues trigger craving

Treatment of Cocaine Dependence

- Is highly individualistic and has variable success
- Principal strategies include inpatient and outpatient programs
- Drug therapy is often used to relieve cocaine craving and mood problems
- Psychological counseling, support, and a highly motivated patient are essential

Cocaine and Pregnancy

- Cocaine babies
  - Microencephaly
  - Reduced birth weight
  - Increased irritability
  - Learning and cognitive defects

Notes

_____

_____

_____

_____

_____

_____

_____

_____

_____

_____

_____

_____

_____

_____

_____

_____

_____

_____

_____

_____

_____

_____

_____

_____

_____

_____

Minor Stimulants

- Caffeine is the most frequently consumed stimulant in the world.
  - It is classified as a xanthine (methylxanthine)
  - It is found in a number of beverages
  - Also found in some OTC medicines and chocolate
- Q: In the U.S., the average daily intake of caffeine is equivalent to _____ cups of coffee a day.
  A: 2 cups of coffee a day

Caffeine Content of Beverages and Chocolate

Beverage	Caffeine Content (mg)/cup	Amount
Brewed coffee	90–125	5 oz.
Instant coffee	35–164	5 oz.
Decaffeinated coffee	1–6	5 oz.
Tea	25–125	5 oz.
Cocoa	5–25	5 oz.
Coca-Cola	45	12 oz.
Pepsi-Cola	38	12 oz.
Mountain Dew	54	12 oz.
Chocolate bar	1–35	1 oz.

Physiological Effects of Xanthines

- CNS effects
  - Enhances alertness, causes arousal, diminishes fatigue
- Adverse CNS effects
  - Insomnia, increase in tension, anxiety, and initiation of muscle twitches
  - Over 500 milligrams—panic sensations, chills, nausea, clumsiness
  - Extremely high doses (5 to 10 grams)— seizures, respiratory failure, and death

Notes

Physiological Effects of Xanthines

Cardiovascular effects
- <u>Low doses</u>—heart activity increases, decreases, or does nothing
- <u>High doses</u>—rate of contraction of the heart increases, minor vasodilation in most of the body, cerebral blood vessels are vasoconstricted

Respiratory system effect
- Can cause air passages to open and facilitate breathing

Physiological Effects of Xanthines
(continued)

- Caffeine intoxication
  - Caffeinism
  - Restlessness, nervousness, excitement, insomnia, flushed face, diuresis, muscle twitching, rambling thoughts and speech, stomach complaints
- Caffeine dependence

OTC Drugs Containing Caffeine or Caffeine-like Stimulants

- Analgesics
- Stay-awake products
- Picker-uppers
- Decongestants
- Herbal stimulants
  - Ephedrine

CHAPTER 11

Tobacco

The chapter outline provides you with an organizational guide to the topics and ideas presented in this chapter of the text.

◎ Key Terms

Define the following terms:

1. *Nicotiana tabacum* _____

2. **Puffing** _____

3. **Tobacco chewing** _____

4. **Clove cigarettes** _____

5. **Emphysema** _____

6. **Chewing tobacco** _____

7. Snuff _____

8. Mainstream smoke _____

9. Passive smoking _____

10. Gateway drug _____

11. Patterns of behavior _____

◎ Fill-in-the-Blank

1. _____ is a colorless, highly volatile liquid alkaloid.

2. Placing a pinch of tobacco between the gums and cheek is called _____

_____.

3. The organic chemical in clove cigarettes that delivers the aroma when inhaled is _____

_____.

4. _____ is the mixture of predominantly sidestream

smoke and exhaled mainstream smoke that is inhaled by the passive smoker.

5. The unexpected and unexplainable death that occurs while infants are sleeping is called _____

_____.

6. Snorting chewing tobacco nasally is called _____.

7. Smoke released into the air from a lighted cigarette is _____.

◎ Identify

1. Identify the three names for the most common type of tobacco used in cigarettes.

    a. _____

    b. _____

    c. _____

2. Identify five factors that determine the amount of nicotine absorbed into the body.

    a. _____

    b. _____

    c. _____

    d. _____

    e. _____

3. Identify and discuss three kinds of smoking cessation aids.

a. _____

b. _____

c. _____

◎ True/False

Tell whether each statement is true or false. If false, explain what makes the statement incorrect.

1. Tobacco use is the leading preventable cause of death in the United States. _____

_____

2. Smoking during pregnancy does not affect the fetus. _____

_____

3. All 50 states have enacted laws that restrict the purchase, possession, or use of tobacco products by

minors. _____

_____

◎ Discussion Questions

1. What efforts has the government made to decrease tobacco use? Do you think these are enough? _____

_____

_____

_____

2. What effects do cigarettes have on the central nervous system? What other effects do cigarettes have on

the body? _____

_____

_____

_____

3. How safe are smokeless tobacco products compared with cigarettes? _____

_____

_____

_____

4. Why do people smoke? _____

_____

_____

_____

5. Should smokers have the right to smoke in public places? Defend your answer. _____

_____

_____

_____

Notes

_____

_____

_____

_____

_____

_____

_____

_____

_____

_____

_____

_____

_____

_____

_____

_____

_____

_____

_____

_____

_____

_____

_____

_____

NINTH EDITION

Glen R. Hanson
Peter J. Venturelli
Annette E. Fleckenstein

Drugs and Society

Tobacco

Chapter 11

Tobacco Use: Scope of the Problem

- Tobacco use is the leading preventable cause of disease and premature death in the U.S.
- 440,000 deaths annually in U.S.
- Tobacco use is the fourth most common risk factor for disease worldwide.

Current Tobacco Use in the U.S.

- In 2003, 70.8 million Americans smoked cigarettes
- 29.8 % of the U.S. population age 12 and older report current use of a tobacco product.
- Males are more likely than females to report the use of any tobacco product

Notes

_____

_____

_____

_____

_____

_____

_____

_____

_____

_____

_____

_____

_____

_____

_____

_____

_____

_____

_____

_____

_____

_____

_____

_____

History of Tobacco Use

- Mayans: tobacco smoke as "divine incense"
- Turkey: poets vs. priests
- France: Louis XIII vs. Louis XIV
- Nicholas Monardes: infallible cure
- Pope Urban VII: excommunication for tobacco users

History in America

- Virginia and *Nicotiana tabacum*
- Chewing and snuffing predominated until the turn of the 20th century
- Flue-curing and puffing

Modern Government Regulation

- 1964—the Advisory Committee to the U.S. Surgeon General reported that cigarette smoking is related to lung cancer
- 1965—Congress passed legislation setting up the National Clearinghouse of Smoking and Health
- 1970—warnings on cigarette labels

Notes

Master Settlement Agreement

• Involved 46 states and a $200 billion settlement

• Regulated outdoor advertisements, clothing, merchandise

• Established a trust fund to compensate tobacco farmers

Pharmacology of Nicotine

• It is a colorless, highly volatile liquid alkaloid.

• When smoked, nicotine enters the lungs and is then absorbed into the bloodstream.

• When chewed or dipped, nicotine is absorbed through the mucous lining of the mouth.

Pharmacology of Nicotine
(continued)

• Amount of tobacco absorbed depends on
  - Exact composition of tobacco
  - How densely the tobacco is packed
  - Whether a filter is used and characteristic of filter
  - The volume of smoke inhaled
  - The number of cigarettes smoked

Notes

_____

_____

_____

_____

_____

_____

_____

_____

_____

_____

_____

_____

_____

_____

_____

_____

_____

_____

_____

_____

_____

_____

_____

Physiological Effects

- In high concentrations, nicotine is highly toxic
- Symptoms of nicotine poisoning
  - Sweating, vomiting, mental confusion, diarrhea, and breathing difficulty
  - Respiratory failure
- Stimulates central dopamine release
- Stimulates CVS by releasing of epinephrine
- Stimulates and then inhibit salivary and bronchial secretions

Other Effects of Nicotine

- Increases respiration because it stimulates receptors in the carotid artery
- Stimulates cardiovascular system by releasing epinephrine
  - Increases heart rate and blood pressure
- Inhibits hunger contractions in the stomach
- Nicotine has been used as an insecticide and at higher concentrations can be extremely toxic

Clove Cigarettes

- Indonesian
- First used by young Americans in the 1980s
- Eugenol—organic chemical that gives a clove its aroma
- Cloves consist of more than 60% tobacco and possess greater amounts of tar, nicotine, and carbon monoxide than regular cigarettes

Mortality Rates

- Tobacco use is the leading preventable cause of death in the U.S.
- On average, adults who smoke die 13–14 years earlier than nonsmokers

Deaths Attributable to Cigarette Smoking: 1995–1999

- 124,813 to lung cancer
- 17,445 to stroke
- 81,976 to ischemic heart disease
- 82,431 to chronic lung disease
- 38,053 to secondhand smoke
- 30,948 to other cancers
- 66,732 to other diagnoses

Chronic Illnesses and Smoking

- Men and women who smoke have more chronic illnesses, including:
  - Emphysema and bronchitis
  - Cardiovascular disease
  - Cancer
  - Bronchopulmonary disease
- Sudden infant death syndrome (SIDS)

Notes

Notes

_____

_____

_____

_____

_____

_____

_____

_____

_____

_____

_____

_____

_____

_____

_____

_____

_____

_____

_____

_____

_____

_____

_____

_____

_____

_____

_____

_____

_____

"Light" Cigarettes

- What are they?
- "Tricking" the machines
- Scientific evidence
- Health effects
- The bottom line…

Tobacco Use Without Smoking

- Dipping, chewing, and snuffing
- In 2003, 10.3 million Americans aged 12 or older used smokeless tobacco
- Increased risk of oral cancer

Secondhand and Sidestream Smoke

- **Mainstream smoke**—smoke drawn through the mouthpiece of the cigarette
- **Sidestream smoke**—smoke released into the air directly from the lighted tip of a cigarette
- **Passive smoking**—nonsmokers' inhalation of tobacco smoke
- **Environmental tobacco smoke**—sidestream smoke and exhaled mainstream smoke that is inhaled by the passive smoker

Notes

Who Smokes?

- Males are more likely than females
- College graduates are the least likely to smoke

Methods for Quitting

- "Cold turkey"
- Behavioral modification
- Smoking cessation aids
  - Nicotine gum
  - Nicotine patches
  - Nicotine nasal spray
  - Nicotine inhalers
  - Bupropion

Social Issues

- Tobacco as a gateway drug

- Smoking prohibition vs. smokers' rights
  - Smoke-free indoor air
  - Youth access to tobacco
  - Licensing
  - Advertising
  - Taxing cigarettes

CHAPTER 12

Hallucinogens (Psychedelics)

The chapter outline provides you with an organizational guide to the topics and ideas presented in this chapter of the text.

Introduction
The History of Hallucinogen Use
    The Native American Church
    Timothy Leary and the League of Spiritual Discovery
Hallucinogen Use Today
The Nature of Hallucinogens
    Sensory and Psychological Effects
    Mechanisms of Action

Types of Hallucinogenic Agents
    Traditional Hallucinogens: LSD Types
    Phenylethylamine Hallucinogens
    Anticholinergic Hallucinogens
    Other Hallucinogens

◎ Key Terms

Define the following terms:

1. Hallucinogens _____

2. Psychotomimetic _____

3. Synesthesia _____

4. Ergotism _____

5. Mydriasis _____

6. Jimsonweed _____

7. Catatonia _____

◎ Fill-in-the-Blank

1. _____ are substances that expand or heighten perception and consciousness.

2. Substances that initiate psychotic behavior are _____.

3. _____ are recurrences of earlier drug-induced sensory experiences in the absence of the drug.

4. _____ are drugs that enhance the sensation and pleasure of touching.

5. Drugs with similar structures are called _____.

◎ Identify

1. Identify the four stages of sensory experiences typically experienced by users of LCD.

a. _____

b. _____

c. _____

d. _____

2. Identify and describe three categories of negative LSD-related flashbacks.

a. _____

b. _____

c. _____

3. What are some effects of using mescaline? _____

_____

_____

4. Briefly discuss the effects of the following hallucinogens:

Psilocybin _____

_____

DMT _____

_____

Nutmeg _____

_____

5. Identify and briefly describe three examples of anticholinergic hallucinogens.

a. _____

b. _____

c. _____

◎ Discussion Questions

1. Should Native Americans be allowed access to otherwise illegal drugs for religious purposes? _____

_____

_____

_____

2. How does LSD affect a user's behavior and perception? _____

_____

_____

_____

3. What dangers does a person face if they decide to take hallucinogenic street drugs? _____

_____

_____

_____

4. Why is MDMA so popular? What are some negative effects of MDMA that users should be aware of? ___

_____

_____

_____

5. Why is PCP considered to be the most dangerous of hallucinogens? _____

_____

_____

_____

Notes

_____

_____

_____

_____

_____

_____

_____

_____

_____

_____

_____

_____

_____

_____

_____

_____

_____

_____

_____

_____

_____

_____

_____

_____

_____

NINTH EDITION

Glen R. Hanson
Peter J. Venturelli
Annette E. Fleckenstein

Drugs and Society

Hallucinogens (Psychedelics)

Chapter 12

Hallucinogens

- Hallucinogens are substances that alter sensory processing in the brain, causing perceptual disturbances, changes in thought processing, and depersonalization

---

History of Hallucinogens

- The Native American Church
  - The American Indian Religious Freedom Act of 1978
- Timothy Leary and the League of Spiritual Discovery
  - _The Psychedelic Experience_

Notes

The Nature of Hallucinogens

- Many drugs can exert hallucinogenic effects
  - Traditional hallucinogens (LSD-types)
  - Phenylethylamines (Ecstasy, amphetamines)
  - Anticholinergic agents (Jimsonweed)
  - Cocaine
  - Steroids

Nature of Hallucinogens

Psychedelic

Psychotogenic

Psychotomimetic

Sensory and Psychological Effects of Hallucinogens

- Altered senses
  - synesthesia
- Loss of control
  - flashbacks
- Self-reflection
  - "make conscious the unconscious"
- Loss of identity and cosmic merging
  - "mystical-spiritual aspect of the drug experience"

Notes

_____

_____

_____

_____

_____

_____

_____

_____

_____

_____

_____

_____

_____

_____

_____

_____

_____

_____

_____

_____

_____

_____

_____

_____

Traditional Hallucinogens: LSD Types of Agents

- LSD (lysergic acid diethylamide), mescaline, psilocybin, dimethyltryptamine (DMT), and myristicin
- These drugs cause predominantly psychedelic effects
- Of high school seniors sampled:
  - 1999—12.2% had used LSD sometime during life
  - 2004—4.6% had used LSD sometime during life

Traditional Hallucinogens: LSD Types of Agents 9 (continued)

- Physical properties of LSD
  - In pure form—colorless, odorless, tasteless
  - Street names—acid, blotter acid, microdot, window panes

Traditional Hallucinogens: LSD Types of Agents (continued)

- Physiological effects
  - Massive increase in neural activity in some brain regions ("electrical storm")
  - Activates sympathetic nervous system (rise in body temp., heart rate, and blood pressure)
  - Parasympathetic nervous system (increase in salivation and nausea)
  - Individuals do not become physically dependent, but psychological dependency can occur

Notes

Traditional Hallucinogens: LSD Types of Agents (continued)

- Effects of this hallucinogen begin 30–90 minutes after ingestion and can last up to 12 hours
- Tolerance to the effects of LSD develops very quickly

Traditional Hallucinogens: LSD Types of Agents (continued)

- Behavioral effects
  - Creativity and insight
  - Adverse psychedelic effects
  - Perceptual effects

Other LSD Types of Agents

- Mescaline (Peyote)
  - Mescaline is the most active drug in peyote; it induces intensified perception of colors and euphoria
  - Effects include dilation of the pupils, increase in body temperature, anxiety, visual hallucinations, alteration of body image, vomiting, muscular relaxation
  - Street samples are rarely authentic

Notes

_____

_____

_____

_____

_____

_____

_____

_____

_____

_____

_____

_____

_____

_____

_____

_____

_____

_____

_____

_____

_____

_____

_____

_____

_____

_____

Other LSD Types of Agents

- Psilocybin
  - Principal source is the *Psilocybe mexicana* mushroom
  - It is not very common on the street
  - Hallucinogenic effects similar to LSD
  - Cross-tolerance among psilocybin, LSD, mescaline
  - Stimulates autonomic nervous system, dilates the pupils, increases body temperature

Other LSD Types of Agents
(continued)

- Dimethyltryptamine (DMT)
  - A short-acting hallucinogen
  - Found in seeds of certain leguminous trees and prepared synthetically
  - It is inhaled and is similar in action to psilocybin

Other LSD Types of Agents

- Foxy
  - Relatively new hallucinogen (not scheduled by DEA)
  - Lower doses—euphoria
  - Higher doses—similar to LSD
- Nutmeg
  - Myristica oil responsible for physical effects
  - High doses can be quite intoxicating
  - Can also cause unpleasant trips

Notes

Phenylethylamine Hallucinogens

- The phenylethylamine drugs are chemically related to amphetamines
- They have varying degrees of hallucinogenic and CNS stimulant effects
  - <u>LSD-like</u>—predominantly release **serotonin**; dominated by their **hallucinogenic** action
  - <u>Cocaine-like</u>—predominantly release **dopamine**; dominated by their **stimulant** effects

---

Phenylethylamine Hallucinogens
(continued)

- Dimthoxymethylamphetamine (DOM or STP)
- "Designer" amphetamines
- 3,4-Methylenedioxyamphetamine (MDA)
- Methylenedioxymethamphetamine (MDMA, Ecstasy)

Anticholinergic Hallucinogens

- The anticholinergic hallucinogens include naturally occurring alkaloid substances that are present in plants and herbs
- The potato family of plants contains most of these mind-altering drugs
- Three potent anticholingergic compounds in these plants
  - Scopolamine
  - Hyoscyamine
  - Atropine

Notes

_____
_____
_____
_____
_____
_____
_____
_____
_____
_____
_____
_____
_____
_____
_____
_____
_____
_____
_____
_____
_____
_____

Naturally Occurring Anticholinergic Hallucinogens

- *Atropa Belladonna*: The Deadly Nightshade
- *Mandragora Officinarum*: The Mandrake
- *Hyoscyamus Niger*: Henbane
- *Datura Stramonium*: Jimsonweed

Other Hallucinogens

- Phencyclidine (PCP)
  - Considered by many experts as the most dangerous of the hallucinogens
  - It was developed as an intravenous anesthetic, but was found to have serious adverse side effects

Other Hallucinogens
(continued)

- Phencyclidine (PCP) physiological effects
  - Hallucinogenic effects, stimulation, depression, anesthesia, analgesia
  - Large doses can cause coma, convulsions, and death
- PCP psychological effects
  - Feelings of strength, power, invulnerability; perceptual distortions, paranoia, violence, psychoses

Other Hallucinogens
(continued)

- Ketamine (general anesthetic)
- Dextromethorphan (cough suppressant)
- Marijuana

Notes

CHAPTER 13

Marijuana

The chapter outline provides you with an organizational guide to the topics and ideas presented in this chapter of the text.

◎ Key Terms

Define the following terms:

1. Perceived risks _____

2. Hashish _____

3. Subjective euphoric effects _____

_____

4. Differential association _____

5. Amotivational syndrome _____

6. Glaucoma _____

7. Altered perceptions _____

8. Anandamide _____

◎ Fill-in-the-Blank

1. The biological species name for the variety of hemp plant known as marijuana is _____

_____.

2. Meaning without seeds, _____ is made from the buds and

flowering tops of female plants and is one of the most potent types of marijuana.

3. _____ involves using the THC in cannabis as a drug to calm or to

relieve symptoms of an illness.

4. Hunger experienced while under the effects of marijuana is called the _____.

5. A compound that is believed to be the cause of sexual arousal is an _____.

◎ Identify

1. Identify three possible medical uses of marijuana.

a. _____

b. _____

c. _____

2. Identify three arguments against using marijuana for medical purposes.

a. _____

b. _____

c. _____

3. Describe the effects of marijuana on the following systems.

a. Central nervous system _____

_____

b. Respiratory system _____

_____

c. Cardiovascular system _____

_____

◎ Discussion Questions

1. How has marijuana been used throughout history? _____

_____

_____

_____

2. Why is marijuana attractive to many individuals? _____

_____

_____

_____

3. Should marijuana be legalized for medical use? Defend your answer. _____

_____

_____

_____

Notes

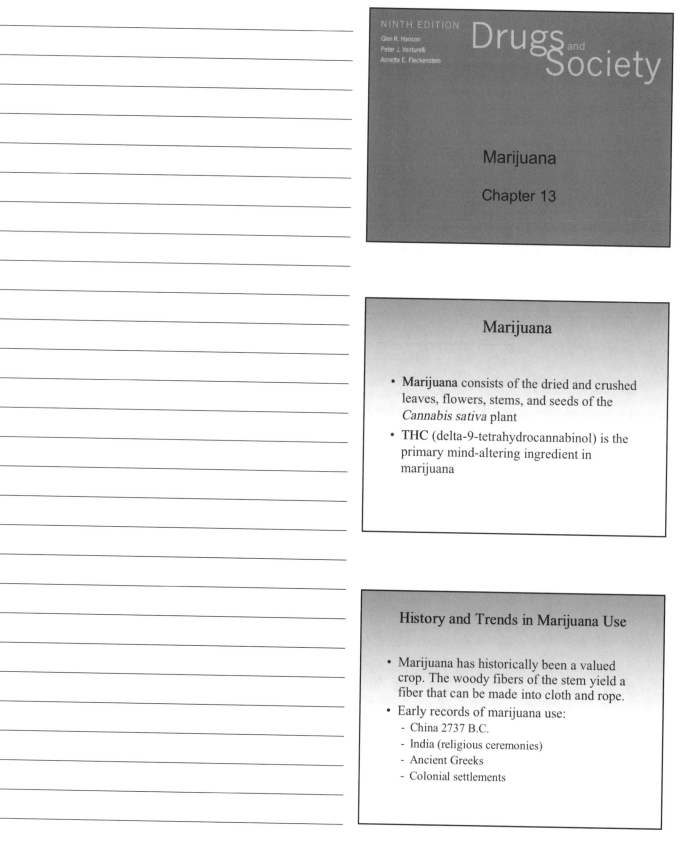

NINTH EDITION
Glen R. Hanson
Peter J. Venturelli
Annette E. Fleckenstein

Drugs and Society

Marijuana

Chapter 13

Marijuana

- **Marijuana** consists of the dried and crushed leaves, flowers, stems, and seeds of the *Cannabis sativa* plant
- **THC** (delta-9-tetrahydrocannabinol) is the primary mind-altering ingredient in marijuana

History and Trends in Marijuana Use

- Marijuana has historically been a valued crop. The woody fibers of the stem yield a fiber that can be made into cloth and rope.
- Early records of marijuana use:
  - China 2737 B.C.
  - India (religious ceremonies)
  - Ancient Greeks
  - Colonial settlements

Notes

Questions and Answers

Q: Today marijuana is how many times more potent than the marijuana on the street in the 1960s and 1970s?

A: Approximately 20 times more potent

Q: How many Americans are current marijuana users?

A: Aged 12 or older in 2001: Out of 19.5 million illicit drug users, *approximately* 55% reported using only marijuana, 21% used marijuana and another illicit drug, and the remaining 25% used an illicit drug but not marijuana in the past month.

Noteworthy Findings Regarding Marijuana Users

- The most highly abused type of illicit drug.
- The highest rate of use was found among young adults (ages 18–25) with 20.3% reporting current use (past month) and among youth (ages 12–17) with 7.9% reporting current use.
- The average age of first use was 17.2 years.
- There were 2.6 million new marijuana users in 2002.

Influencing Factors

- **Structural factors**
  - Age, gender, family background, lack of religious beliefs
- **Social and interactional factors**
  - Type of interpersonal relationships, friendship cliques, drug use within the peer group setting
- **Setting**
  - Type of community and neighborhood (physical location of drug use)
- **Attitudinal factors**
  - Personal attitudes toward the use of drugs, self esteem, maturation level, etc.

Notes

_____

_____

_____

_____

_____

_____

_____

_____

_____

_____

_____

_____

_____

_____

_____

_____

_____

_____

_____

_____

_____

_____

_____

_____

Marijuana

- Gateway drugs
  - Drugs that often lead to the use of more addictive types of drugs
  - Alcohol, tobacco, and marijuana are the drugs most commonly believed to be gateway drugs
  - Other common gateway drugs include inhalants and anabolic steroids.

Varieties of Marijuana from the Cannabis Sativa Plant

- **Hashish**
  - Average concentration of THC is 3.6.% to 28%
- **Ganja**
  - Consists of the dried tops of female plants
- *Sinsemilla* (without seeds), **"hydro"** (grown in water), **kine bud, dro, 30s,** and **blueberry** (more recent names of popular types of marijuana)
  - Average concentration of THC is 7.5% and higher
- **Bhang**
  - Average concentration of THC is 1% to 2%

Behavioral Effects

- Low to moderate doses produce euphoria and a pleasant state of relaxation
- Common effects: dry mouth, elevated heartbeat, some loss of coordination and balance, slower reaction times, reddening of the eyes, elevated blood pressure, some mental confusion (short-term memory loss)
- A typical high lasts from 2 to 3 hours (length of effects depends on amount of THC), and the user experiences altered perception of space and time as well as impaired memory

Notes

Behavioral Effects
(continued)

- An acute dose of cannabis can produce adverse reactions: mild anxiety to panic and paranoia.
- In a minority of cases users can exhibit psychoses, delusional and bizarre behavior, and hallucinations. These reactions occur most frequently in individuals who are under stress, anxious, depressed, or borderline schizophrenic, and are using the more potent types of marijuana.

Behavioral Effects
(continued)

- Subjective euphoric effect
  - Associated with marijuana use are the ongoing social and psychological experiences incurred while intoxicated with marijuana. These include both the user's altered state of consciousness and his/her perceptions while intoxicated.
  - Differential association
    - Behavioral satisfaction derived from friends who use marijuana ("fun-times when high with friends").

Driving Performance

- The ability to perform complex tasks, such as driving, is often impaired while under the influence of marijuana.
- In limited surveys, from 70% to 80% of marijuana users indicate that they sometimes drive while being high.
- A 1998 study found that of 1800 blood samples taken from drivers arrested for driving while intoxicated, 19% tested positive for marijuana.

Notes

_____

_____

_____

_____

_____

_____

_____

_____

_____

_____

_____

_____

_____

_____

_____

_____

_____

_____

_____

_____

_____

_____

_____

_____

_____

Critical Thinking Skills

- Marijuana has been found to have a negative impact on critical thinking skills.
- Alertness, memory, and learning are impaired under the use of marijuana.
- The unresolved question is whether these impairments are short term or long term.

Amotivational Syndrome

- **Amotivational Syndrome** refers to a belief that heavy use of marijuana causes a lack of motivation and reduced productivity. Specifically, users show apathy, a poor short-term memory, difficulty with concentration, and a lingering disinterest in pursuing goals.

Therapeutic Uses of Marijuana

Medical marijuana use—Involves using the THC derived from smoking marijuana or using Marinol,* in cannabis as a drug to calm or relieve symptoms of an illness

Some research shows that THC can be used for treating:

- Glaucoma
  - Potentially blinding eye disease causing continual and increasing intraocular pressure

*Marinol is an FDA-approved THC in capsule form (dronabinol)

Notes

Therapeutic Uses of Marijuana (continued)

- Appetite stimulant—patients experiencing anorexia, AIDS, chemotherapy and radiation therapy
- Antiseizure—aids in the prevention of seizures (epilepsy)
- Muscle relaxation—aids in muscle spasms
- Analgesic effect—in patients experiencing frequent migraines and chronic headaches or inflammation

Arguments Against Marijuana Use

- It contains 421 chemicals.
- It is stronger than it was 20 years ago.
- It is far worse for the lungs than tobacco.
- It causes "amotivational syndrome."
- It is illegal and use is not approved by the federal government. (Federal government believes it has no medically proven use.)

Physiological Effects

- Central Nervous System
- Respiratory System
- Cardiovascular System
- Sexual Performance and Reproduction

Notes

_____

_____

_____

_____

_____

_____

_____

_____

_____

_____

_____

_____

_____

_____

_____

_____

_____

_____

_____

_____

_____

_____

Effects of Marijuana on the Central Nervous System

- Altered perceptions
  - Changes in the interpretation of stimuli resulting from marijuana use
- "Munchies"
  - Hunger experienced while under the effects of marijuana
- Anandamide
  - Possible neurotransmitter acting at the marijuana (cannabinoid) receptor site

Effects on Other Systems

- Alveolar Macrophages (Respiratory System)
  - Special white blood cells that play a role in cleaning lung tissue are less able to remove debris when exposed to smoke
- Vasodilation (Cardiovascular System)
  - Enlarged blood vessels
- Aphrodisiac (Sexual Performance and Reproduction)
  - Refers to a compound (in marijuana, THC is believed to cause sexual arousal)

DSM-IV Regarding Cannabis Dependence

- Cannabis dependence is characterized by "compulsive use" in acquiring and spending hours per day using the substance. These users persist in their use despite knowledge of physical problems (for example, chronic cough related to smoking) or psychological problems (for example, excessive sedation resulting from repeated use of high doses; APA 1994).

CHAPTER 14

Inhalants

The chapter outline provides you with an organizational guide to the topics and ideas presented in this chapter of the text.

Introduction
History of Inhalants
Types of Inhalants
    Volatile Substances
    Anesthetics
    Nitrites

Current Patterns and Signs of Abuse
    Adolescent and Teenage Usage
    Gender, Race, Socioeconomics, and Abuse
    Signs of Inhalant Abuse
Dangers of Inhalant Abuse
Treatment of Abuse

◎ Key Terms

Define the following terms:

1. Volatile _____

2. Euphorigenic _____

◎ Fill-in-the-Blank

1. An irregular heartbeat is called an _____.

2. _____ is a state of oxygen deficiency.

3. Gasoline is an example of a _____ substance and is abused commonly by

young people due to its widespread availability.

◎ Identify

1. Give four signs of inhalant abuse.

    a. _____

b. _____

c. _____

d. _____

2. Name four of the thousands of products misused as inhalants today.

a. _____

b. _____

c. _____

d. _____

3. Identify and discuss the three major groups of inhalants.

a. _____

b. _____

c. _____

◎ Discussion Questions

1. Why are inhalants popular? Give several reasons. _____

_____

_____

_____

2. Why is inhalant abuse such a serious problem? What are the dangers and misconceptions associated with inhalant abuse? _____

_____

_____

_____

3. Why is it often difficult to treat inhalant abuse? _____

_____

_____

_____

Notes

_____

_____

_____

_____

_____

_____

_____

_____

_____

_____

_____

_____

_____

_____

_____

_____

_____

_____

_____

_____

_____

_____

_____

_____

_____

_____

_____

_____

NINTH EDITION

Glen R. Hanson
Peter J. Venturelli
Annette E. Fleckenstein

Drugs and Society

Inhalants

Chapter 14

Inhalants

- Volatile substances
- Introduced via lungs
- Intoxicating; euphorigenic

Who Abuses?

- Seventeen percent of all U.S. 8th graders have misused an inhalant at least once in their lifetime.
- Inhalants are among the most commonly used drugs by adolescents.

Notes

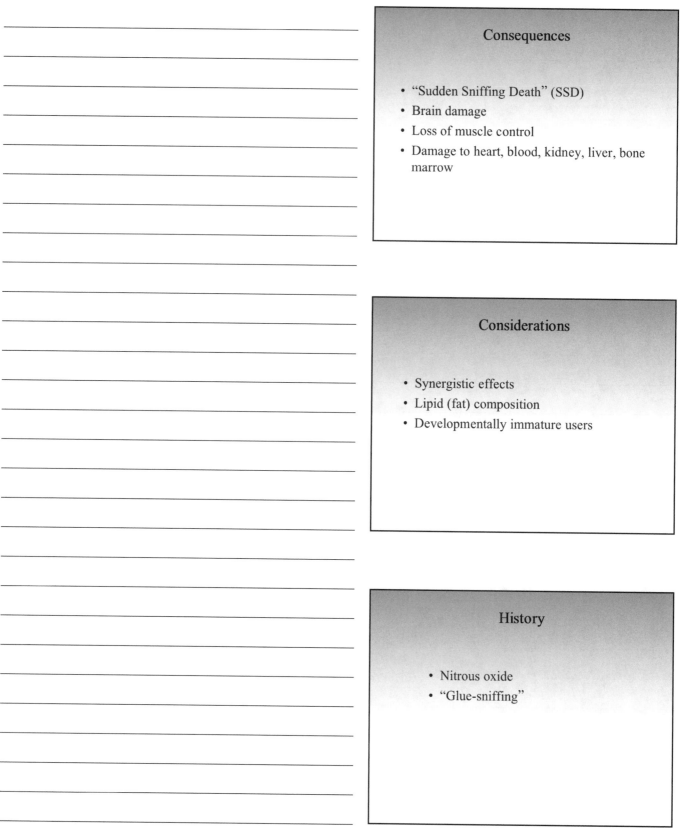

Consequences

- "Sudden Sniffing Death" (SSD)
- Brain damage
- Loss of muscle control
- Damage to heart, blood, kidney, liver, bone marrow

Considerations

- Synergistic effects
- Lipid (fat) composition
- Developmentally immature users

History

- Nitrous oxide
- "Glue-sniffing"

Notes

Classification

- Volatile substances
- Anesthetics
- Nitrites

Effects of Volatile Substances

- Nausea
- Cough/sneeze
- Light-headedness
- Damage heart, kidneys, brain
- Hypoxia/death

Aerosols

- Propellant gases
- Psychoactive effects can be caused by solvents used to dissolve products
- Concentrate chemicals

Notes

Toluene

- Brain, liver, and kidney damage
- Arrhythmias
- "Sudden sniffing death"

Other Volatile Substances

- Butane
- Propane
- Gasoline
- Freon

Anesthetics

- Nitrous oxide
- "Laughing gas"
- "Whippets"
- Generally not significant abuse problem

Nitrites

- Vasodilators
- "Poppers"
- Room deodorizers
- Abused by only a few, select groups

Why Abused?

- Legally obtained
- Readily available
- Inexpensive
- Easy to conceal
- Lack of information about potential dangers

Who Abuses?

- Seventeen percent of all U.S. 8th graders have misused an inhalant at least once in their lifetime
- Kid's habit
- Even small children
- Rates of past year use were similar among females and males aged 12–17
- Often poor self-image, difficult environment (but not always…)

Notes

Notes

_____

_____

_____

_____

_____

_____

_____

_____

_____

_____

_____

_____

_____

_____

_____

_____

_____

_____

_____

_____

_____

_____

Some Signs of Abuse

- Appear drunken
- Red, watery eyes
- "Sniffles" without other signs of cold
- Slurred speech
- Rashes on nose and mouth

Other Signs…

- Unusual chemicals in belongings
- Solvent-smelling breath
- Sitting with marker near nose
- Constantly smelling clothes
- Hiding chemical-soaked rags

Dangers of Inhalants

- Sudden sniffing death syndrome
- Damage brain, liver, kidney, heart, fetus
- Accidents associated with "intoxication" and fires

Treatment

- Treatment programs
- Education
- Prevention

Notes

CHAPTER 15

Over-the-Counter (OTC), Prescription, and Herbal Drugs

The chapter outline provides you with an organizational guide to the topics and ideas presented in this chapter of the text.

Introduction
OTC Drugs
Abuse of OTC Drugs
Federal Regulation of OTC Drugs
OTC Drugs and Self-Care
Types of OTC Drugs
OTC Herbal (Natural) Products

Prescription Drugs
Prescription Drug Abuse
Proper Doctor-Patient Communication
Drug Selection: Generic Versus Proprietary
Common Categories of Prescription Drugs

◎ Key Terms

Define the following terms:

1. **Analgesics** _____

2. **Salicylates** _____

3. **Anti-inflammatory** _____

4. **NSAIDs** _____

5. **Congestive rebound** _____

6. **Gastritis** _____

7. **Keratolytics** _____

8. **SPF number** _____

9. **Monoamine oxidase inhibitors (MAOIs)** _____

10. **Diabetes mellitus** _____

11. **Peptic ulcers** _____

12. Hypertension _____

13. Ischemia _____

14. Angina pectoris _____

15. Edema _____

◎ Fill-in-the-Blank

1. _____ are potent hormones released from the adrenal glands.

2. Drugs that reduce fevers are _____.

3. _____ is a potentially fatal complication of colds, flu, or chicken pox in children.

4. Drugs that block the coughing reflex are _____.

5. Substances that stimulate mucous secretion and diminish mucous viscosity are _____ _____.

6. _____ are drugs that suppress the activity of the brain's appetite center, causing reduced food intake.

7. The outermost protective layer of the skin is the _____.

8. The most commonly used group of drugs to treat severe depression are _____ _____.

9. Drugs taken by mouth to treat type II diabetes are _____ _____.

10. _____ is a disease consisting of spontaneous, repetitive seizures.

11. Drugs that widen air passages are called _____.

12. _____ occurs when the heart is unable to pump sufficient blood for the body's needs.

13. _____ occurs when the thyroid gland does not produce sufficient hormone.

◎ Identify

1. Identify six kinds of information that must appear on the labels of an OTC medicinal product.

　　a. _____

b. _____

c. _____

d. _____

e. _____

f. _____

2. Identify three types of drugs used to treat the common cold. Indicate the symptoms for which each drug is used.

a. _____

b. _____

c. _____

3. Identify three common over-the-counter drugs and their uses.

a. _____

b. _____

c. _____

4. Identify the criteria, according to the Durham-Humphrey Amendment of 1951, to determine if a drug should be controlled with prescriptions.

a. _____

b. _____

c. _____

d. _____

5. Identify five signs of patients with drug-seeking behavior.

a. _____

b. _____

c. _____

d. _____

e. _____

6. Identify three common categories of prescription drugs and explain their uses.

a. _____

b. _____

c. _____

◎ True/False

Tell whether the statement is true or false. If false, explain what makes the statement incorrect.

1. OTC drugs are always safe and effective for consumer use. _____

_____

◎ Discussion Questions

1. What are some concerns about the FDA's switching policy? Do you think switching prescription drugs to OTC status is a safe decision? Defend your answer._____

_____

_____

_____

2. Why does abuse of OTC products often occur? _____

_____

_____

_____

3. What rules should be followed to ensure safe OTC drug use? _____

_____

_____

_____

4. What regulation is placed on OTC herbal products? Should there be more? Are these products safe? __

_____

_____

_____

5. Why is it important to communicate with your doctor? What questions should you ask to ensure that you are being given appropriate prescriptions?_____

_____

_____

_____

6. How do generic drugs compare to proprietary ones? _____

_____

_____

_____

7. What is the difference between Type I and Type II diabetes? _____

_____

_____

_____

Notes

Prescription & OTC Drugs

- <u>Prescription</u> drugs are available only by recommendation of an authorized health professional, such as a physician.
- <u>Nonprescription</u> (over-the-counter, or OTC) drugs are available on request and do not require approval by a health professional.

Prescription & OTC Drugs
(continued)

- Prescription and OTC drugs have been viewed differently by the public since the classifications were established by the Durham-Humphrey Amendment of 1951.
- In general, the public views <u>OTC drugs</u> as less effective, safe, and rarely abused and <u>prescription</u> drugs as more potent and frequently dangerous.
- However, these distinctions are not always accurate.

Notes

OTC Drugs Interesting Facts

- Each year, people in the U.S. spend over $14 billion on OTC drugs
- More than 300,000 different OTC products are available on the market
- OTC expenditures comprise 60% of the annual drug purchases in the U.S.
- An estimated 3 out of 4 people routinely self-medicate with these drug products

---

Abuse of OTC Drugs

- OTC products generally have a greater margin of safety than their prescription counterparts, but issues of abuse need to be considered
- Physical dependence
- Psychological dependence

Abuse of OTC Drugs
(continued)

- Nonprescription products that can be quite habit-forming: decongestants, laxatives, antihistamines, sleep aids, and antacids
- OTC drugs are more likely to be abused by members of the general public who inadvertently become dependent due to excessive self-medication, than by hard-core drug addicts

Notes

_____

_____

_____

_____

_____

_____

_____

_____

_____

_____

_____

_____

_____

_____

_____

_____

_____

_____

_____

_____

_____

_____

_____

_____

_____

"Switching" Policy of the FDA

- The FDA is attempting to make more drugs available to the general public by switching some frequently used and safe prescription medications to OTC status.
- There have been approximately 70 active ingredients switched, leading to more than 700 new OTC drug products.

OTC Drugs and Self-Care

- Many of the major health problems in the United States can be treated with OTC medications.
- If done correctly, self-care with OTC medications can provide significant relief from minor, self-limiting health problems at minimal cost.

OTC Labels

- Required label information includes:
    - Approved uses of the product
    - Detailed instructions on safe and effective use
    - Cautions or warnings to those at greatest risk when taking the medication

Notes

Label Information Controlled by the FDA

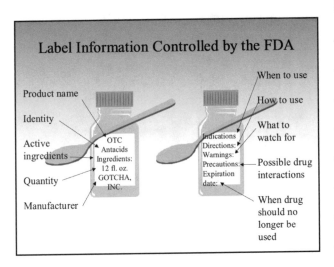

Product name
Identity
Active ingredients
Quantity
Manufacturer

OTC Antacids Ingredients: 12 fl. oz. GOTCHA, INC.

When to use
How to use
What to watch for

Indications
Directions:
Warnings:
Precautions:
Expiration date:

Possible drug interactions

When drug should no longer be used

Rules for Proper OTC Drug Use

- Always know what you are taking.
- Know the effects.
- Read and heed the warnings and cautions.
- Don't use anything for more than 1 to 2 weeks.
- Be particularly cautious if also taking prescription drugs or herbal products.
- If you have questions, ask a pharmacist.
- If you don't need it, don't use it!

Types of OTC Drugs

- Internal analgesics
  - Salicylates
  - Acetaminophen
  - Ibuprofen
  - Ibuprofen-like
- Therapeutic considerations
  - Analgesic actions
  - Anti-inflammatory effects
  - Antipyretic effects
  - Side effects

Notes

_____

_____

_____

_____

_____

_____

_____

_____

_____

_____

_____

_____

_____

_____

_____

_____

_____

_____

_____

_____

_____

_____

_____

_____

Types of OTC Drugs
(continued)

- Cold, allergy and cough remedies
  - Decongestants
  - Antitussives
  - Expectorants
  - Vitamin C
- Sleep aids
  - Antihistamines
  - Melatonin
- Stimulants
  - Stay-awake or energy-promoting

Types of OTC Drugs
(continued)

- Gastrointestinal medication
  - Antacids and anti-heartburn medication
- Diet aids
- Skin products
  - Acne medications
  - Sun products
- Skin first-aid products
- OTC herbal products

Prescription Drugs

- There are currently more than 10,000 prescription products sold in the United States, representing:
  - Approximately 1500 different drugs
  - With 20 to 50 new medications approved each year by the FDA

Notes

Prescription Drugs
(continued)

- According to the Durham-Humphrey Amendment of 1951, drugs are controlled with prescription if they are
  - Habit-forming
  - Not safe for self-medication
  - Intended to treat ailments that require the supervision of a health professional
  - New and without an established safe track record

Prescription Drug Abuse

- Over 11 million Americans use prescription drugs for nonmedical purposes each year
- Three classes most likely to be abused
  - Narcotic analgesics
  - CNS depressants
  - Stimulants

Prescription Drug Abuse
(continued)

- Illicit use of prescription drugs may be prompted by several reasons
  - To relieve withdrawal caused by drug habits
  - To treat infections caused by drug abuse
  - To provide a source of fresh, clean needles for injecting drugs of abuse
  - To prolong high caused by drugs of abuse

Notes

_____

_____

_____

_____

_____

_____

_____

_____

_____

_____

_____

_____

_____

_____

_____

_____

_____

_____

_____

_____

_____

_____

_____

_____

_____

Doctor–Patient Communication

- When a physician prescribes a drug, a patient should insist on answers to the following questions:
  - What is being treated?
  - What is the desired outcome?
  - What are the possible side effects of the drug?
  - How should the drug be taken to minimize problems and maximize benefits?

Generic Versus Proprietary Drugs

- *Generic*—the official, nonpatented, nonproprietary name of a drug. The term *generic* is used by the public to refer to the common name of a drug that is not subject to trademark rights.
- *Proprietary*—a brand or trademark name that is registered with the U.S. Patent Office. Proprietary denoted medications are marketed under specific brand names, i.e., Valium.

Common Categories of Prescription Drugs

- Analgesics
  - Nonsteroidal anti-inflammatory (NSAIDS)
  - Narcotic analgesics
- Antibiotics
  - Antibacterials
- Antidepressants

Common Categories of Prescription Drugs (continued)

- Antidiabetic drugs
- Antiepileptic drugs
- Antiulcer drugs
- Bronchodilators

Common Categories of Prescription Drugs (continued)

- Cardiovascular drugs
  - Antihypertensive agents
  - Antianginal agents
  - Drugs to treat congestive heart failure
  - Cholesterol and lipid-lowering drugs
- Hormone-related drugs
- Sedative-hypnotic agents
- Drugs to treat HIV

Notes

CHAPTER 16

Drug Use Within Major Subcultures

The chapter outline provides you with an organizational guide to the topics and ideas presented in this chapter of the text.

◎ Key Terms

Define the following terms:

1. Subculture _____

2. Outsider's perspective _____

3. Insider's perspective _____

4. Ergogenic _____

5. Anabolic steroids _____

6. "Cycling" _____

7. "Pyramiding" _____

8. Human growth factor _____

9. Sociobiological changes _____

10. Rohypnol _____

11. Protease inhibitors _____

12. Highly active antiretroviral therapy (HAART) _____

_____

◎ Fill-in-the-Blank

1. Using performance-enhancing drugs to increase athletic ability is called _____

_____.

2. _____ are naturally occurring male hormones, such as

testosterone.

3. Use of several types of steroids at the same time is called _____

_____.

4. _____ involves developing tolerance to the effects of anabolic

steroids.

5. The use of other drugs while taking anabolic steroids to avoid possible side effects is known as an _____

_____.

6. A "designer drug" synthetic version of human growth factor (HGF) is _____

_____.

7. _____ is the drug most widely used and abused by women

in the United States.

8. _____ violence occurs between members of the same gang, while

_____ occurs between members of different gangs.

◎ Identify

1. Why would individuals within various subcultures initially turn to drugs? Provide three internal subculture forces and three external subculture forces.

   Internal Subculture Forces

   a. _____

   b. _____

   c. _____

   External Subculture Forces

   a. _____

   b. _____

   c. _____

2. Identify four possible adverse effects of heavy steroid use.

   a. _____

   b. _____

   c. _____

   d. _____

3. What attracts adolescents to gangs? Identify five things that gangs offer often troubled adolescents.

   a. _____

   b. _____

   c. _____

   d. _____

   e. _____

4. How can one prevent adolescent gang involvement? Offer three suggestions.

   a. _____

   b. _____

   c. _____

5. Identify five behaviors that act as warning signs that adolescents may be abusing drugs.

   a. _____

   b. _____

   c. _____

   d. _____

   e. _____

◎ Discussion Questions

1. Why do athletes often risk using drugs? _____

_____

_____

_____

2. What is the ATLAS program? Is this program an effective tool for the prevention of steroid use by

athletes? _____

_____

_____

_____

3. How do the roles of females in society affect their drug use? _____

_____

_____

_____

4. Why are women less likely than men to seek treatment for, and rehabilitation from, drug dependence?

_____

_____

_____

5. Why do adolescents use drugs? _____

_____

_____

_____

6. How are patterns of drug use in adolescents different from drug use patterns in adults? _____

_____

_____

_____

7. How does drug use contribute to teen suicide? _____

_____

_____

_____

8. Why do college students use drugs? _____

_____

_____

_____

9. How does AIDS relate to drug abuse? _____

_____

_____

_____

10. How does the entertainment industry affect drug use? _____

_____

_____

_____

11. Discuss the increasing role of the Internet in drug abuse. _____

_____

_____

_____

Notes

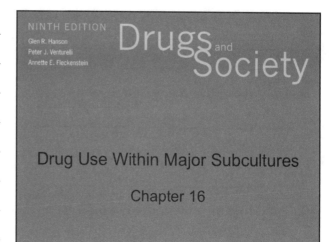

NINTH EDITION

Glen R. Hanson
Peter J. Venturelli
Annette E. Fleckenstein

Drugs and Society

Drug Use Within Major Subcultures

Chapter 16

Subculture

- A **subculture** is defined as a subgroup within the population whose members share similar values and patterns of related behaviors that differ from the larger population.
- **Internal subcultural forces**—shared attitudes about drug use, habitual and/or addictive behavior, etc.
- **External subcultural forces**—law enforcement, availability of drug dealers, concerns with being caught using drugs, etc.

Views About Drug Use/Abuse

- **Outsider's Perspective**
  - Viewing a group or subculture from outside the group and viewing the group and its members as an observer; looking "in." Nonusers viewing drug users.
- **Insider's Perspective**
  - Viewing a group or subculture from inside the group; seeing members as they perceive themselves. Drug users in agreement with other drug users or sympathizers.

Notes

Athletes and Drug Abuse

- Studies have shown that athletes are *not* more likely than nonathletes to use drugs of abuse such as marijuana, alcohol, barbiturates, cocaine, and hallucinogens. However, athletes are much more likely than other subcultures of drug users to take drugs (ergogenic drugs) to enhance performance.

Drugs Used by Athletes

- **Anabolic steroids** consist of a group of natural and synthetic drugs that are chemically similar to cholesterol and related to the male hormone testosterone.
- Naturally occurring male hormones, or **androgens** are produced by the testes in males.

Abuse of Anabolic Steroids by Athletes

- Under some conditions, androgen-like drugs can increase muscle mass and strength
- It is estimated that as many as 1 million Americans have used or are currently using these drugs to achieve a "competitive edge"
- Two percent of college-age men
- 6.7% of male high school athletes
- 1% of female high school athletes

Notes

_____

_____

_____

_____

_____

_____

_____

_____

_____

_____

_____

_____

_____

_____

_____

_____

_____

_____

_____

_____

_____

_____

_____

_____

_____

Steroid Use by Children and Adolescents

- 52,000 American *children* and adolescents are using anabolic steroids.
- One study in the journal *Pediatrics* found that in Massachusetts middle schools, 2.7% of athletes were using steroids (Begley et al. 1999, p.54).
- Another source found that males are much more likely to use and abuse steroids than females (NIDA, 2004).

Patterns of Anabolic Steroid Use by Athletes

- **Stacking**—use of several types of steroids at the same time.
- **Cycling**—use of different steroids taken singly, but in sequence.
- **Plateauing**—developing tolerance to a particular steroid.
- **Pyramiding**—beginning steroid use with low doses moving to higher doses, then reducing the dosage at the end of the cycle.
- **Array**—use of other drugs while taking anabolic steroids to avoid possible side effects, such as taking diuretics, antiacne, antiestrogens.

Effects of Anabolic Steroids

- Increase strength
- Gain in lean body mass
- Increase "bad" blood cholesterol
- Increased risk of liver disorders
- Psychological effects (irritability, outbursts of anger—"road rage," mania, psychosis, and major depression)
- Psychological and physical dependence with continual use of high doses

Notes

Effects of Anabolic Steroids
(continued)

- Withdrawal symptoms—craving, fatigue, depression, restlessness, loss of appetite, insomnia, diminished sex drive, headaches
- Alterations in reproductive systems and sex hormones (breast enlargement in males, breast reduction and hair growth in females, infertility, and atrophy—shrinkage of penis and testicles in males and enlargement of external genitalia in females)

Effects of Anabolic Steroids
(continued)

- Stunted growth in adolescents, deepening of voice in females, water retention
- Change in skin and hair (severe acne, male pattern baldness, and increased body hair)
- Persistent unpleasant breath odor
- Swelling of feet and limbs

Drugs Used by Athletes

- Stimulants (amphetamines and cocaine)
- Clenbuterol
- Erythropoietin
- Human growth factor (HGF) and human growth hormone (HGH)
- ß (Beta)-adrenergic blockers
- Gamma-hydroxybutyrate

Notes

_____

_____

_____

_____

_____

_____

_____

_____

_____

_____

_____

_____

_____

_____

_____

_____

_____

_____

_____

_____

_____

_____

Drug Use Among Women

- Overall, females consistently use fewer licit and illicit drugs (29% of females versus 34% of males use illicit drugs).
- More males (29%) than females (22%) use marijuana on a yearly basis.
- Males (84%) and females (83%) are nearly equal with regard to the consumption of alcohol. However, with regard to binge drinking, greater differences exist between males (45%) than females (27%).
- Females (3.3%) are less likely to use hallucinogen-type drugs than males (6.5%). Similarly with cocaine use females (5%), males (8.2%).
- Steroid use among young adults is much more prevalent among males than females.

Q. How do the following drugs affect a woman's reproduction?

- Cocaine?
- Alcohol?
- Tobacco?
- Other drugs (marijuana, LSD, other depressant drugs)?

Women and Alcohol

- Alcohol is the drug most widely used and abused by women in the U.S.
  - Women aged 12 and older—42.3% used alcohol in the past month and 19.4 reported binge drinking
  - Unlike men, women are less likely to develop severe alcohol dependence (only 25% of the alcoholics in the U.S. are female)
- Women dependent on alcohol are judged more harshly than men dependent on alcohol

Notes

Why Adolescents Use Drugs

- Most adolescents who use substances of abuse during psychosocial development do not develop problematic drug dependence.
- Adolescent users who have difficulty with drugs often lack coping skills, are from dysfunctional families, maintain poor self-images, and/or feel socially and emotionally insecure.

Why Adolescents Use Drugs
(continued)

- Parents who are most likely to foster drug abusing children are
  - Drug abusers themselves
  - Excessively rigid and condemning
  - Overly demanding
  - Overly protective
  - Overwhelmed with their own personal conflicts
  - Unable to effectively communicate with their children

Why Adolescents Use Drugs
(continued)

- Recent research indicates that the most important factor influencing drug use among adolescents is peer drug use.
- Research also shows that there exists a correlation between strong family bonds and non-drug-using peer groups.
- Use drugs to cope with boredom, unpleasant feelings, emotions, and stress or to relieve depression, reduce tension, and reduce alienation.
- *What other explanations can you offer that may explain why adolescents use drugs?*

Notes

_____

_____

_____

_____

_____

_____

_____

_____

_____

_____

_____

_____

_____

_____

_____

_____

_____

_____

_____

_____

_____

_____

_____

Patterns of Drug Use in Adolescents

- Fill in the blanks regarding recent surveys on lifetime drug patterns of 8th graders in 2004.
  A.__% had used alcohol
  B.__% had used cigarettes
  C.__% had used inhalants
  D.__% had used marijuana

Key: A is 22%, B is 28%, C is 17%, and D is 16%.

Patterns of Drug Use in Adolescents
(continued)

- Fill in the blanks regarding recent surveys (2004) on lifetime drug patterns of 12th graders.
  A. __% had used alcohol
  B. __% had used cigarettes
  C. __% had used inhalants
  D. __% had used marijuana

Key: A is 51%, B is 53%, C is 11%, and D is 46%.

Consequences of Adolescent Drug Use

- Adolescent suicide
- Sexual violence and drugs
- Gangs and drugs

Notes

Prevention and Treatment of Adolescent Drug Problems

- Encourage parental awareness of gangs.
- Encourage alternative participation in organizations or groups (athletics, school activities, career development, or involvement volunteering programs).
- Help children to develop coping skills regarding frustration and stress.
- Educate children about gang-related problems and help them understand that like drugs, gangs are the result of problems and are not the solutions to problems.

Major Reasons Cited by College Students for Their Drug Use*

- To have fun (78.9%)
- To relieve stress (63.9%)
- To ease social interactions (53.8%)

*Sample survey of 1232 male and female college students and their use of alcohol and other drugs

Drug Use by College Students

- Most popular substance use and abuse is alcohol (81.7% of college students).
- College students who frequently binge drink are more likely to smoke cigarettes and use illegal drugs as well.
- A clear relationship exists between alcohol use and grade point average (GPA). (The more alcohol consumed the lower the GPA.)

Notes

_____

_____

_____

_____

_____

_____

_____

_____

_____

_____

_____

_____

_____

_____

_____

_____

_____

_____

_____

_____

_____

_____

_____

_____

_____

_____

Drug Use by College Students (continued)

- Almost **half** of college students who were victims of campus crimes said they were drinking or using other drugs when they were victimized.
- Researchers estimate that alcohol use is implicated in one- to two-thirds of sexual assault and acquaintance or date rape cases among teens and college students.

Drug Use by College Students (continued)

- Full-time college students (81.7%) are more likely to use alcohol than others (76.7%); (others are defined as respondents that are one to four years beyond high school but not full-time students).
- Thirty-nine percent binged on alcohol.
- Whites are highest binge drinkers followed by blacks and then Asians.
- High percentage of drinkers (approx. 50%) had altercations with law enforcement officials while consuming extraordinary amounts of alcohol.

Drug Use by College Students (continued)

- Fill in the blanks regarding recent surveys on lifetime drug patterns of full-time college students.
  A.__% had used alcohol
  B.__% had used cigarettes
  C.__% had used MDMA (Ecstasy)
  D.__% had used marijuana

Key: A is 82%, B is 35%, C is 4.4%, and D is 34%.

Summary Findings: Drug Use and College Students

Modest Percentage *Increased* Usage from 2000 to 2003:
- Any illicit drug other than marijuana
- LSD (steep drop in percentage using, 4.3% in 2000 to 1.4% in 2003)
- Cocaine (4.8% in 2000 to 5.4% in 2003) and crack use
- Other narcotics, OxyContin and Vicodin
- Tranquilizers (4.2% in 2000 to 6.9% in 2003)
- Sedatives (barbiturates) (3.7% in 2000 to 4.1% in 2003)

Summary Findings: Drug Use and College Students (continued)

- Modest percentage *decreased* usage from 2000 to 2003:
  - Cigarettes (41.3% in 2000 to 35.2% in 2003)
  - MDMA (Ecstasy) (9.1% in 2000 to 4.4% in 2003)
- Not much change (stable percentages in usage) 2000–2003:
  - Alcohol
  - Marijuana
  - Hallucinogens
  - Amphetamines

HIV and AIDS: The Disease

- Nature of HIV infection and related symptoms
- Diagnosis and treatment
  - Protease inhibitors
  - Highly active antiretroviral therapy (HAART) (most recent types of medications used to treat HIV/AIDS-infected individuals)
- Who is most at risk for HIV?
  A. ___% men having sex with men
  B. ___% of injection drug users
  C. ___% heterosexual contact
  Key: A is 54%, B is 23%, and C is 15%.

Notes

Notes

_____

_____

_____

_____

_____

_____

_____

_____

_____

_____

_____

_____

_____

_____

_____

_____

_____

_____

_____

_____

_____

_____

_____

_____

_____

Findings Regarding Age at Diagnosis of HIV and AIDS

- HIV is fifth leading cause of death for all Americans between ages of 25 and 44.
- For black men and women, HIV is the number one cause of death.
- In the U.S., 77% of all people affected with AIDS are male and 23% are female. Worldwide, 73 women are infected for every 100 infected men.
- New York, Florida, Texas, and North Carolina reported the highest number of persons with HIV infection in 2003 (CDCP 2004). Most people with AIDS are found in metropolitan areas with populations of 500,000 or more.

Leading Causes for the Spread of HIV/AIDS in the U.S.

- Intravenous drug use of heroin, cocaine, or both—most important factor for the spread of HIV/AIDS
- Crack—encourages high-risk sexual activities

Adolescents / Youth and AIDS

In 2002, male adolescents between the ages of 13–19 who were diagnosed with AIDS contracted the disease in the following ways:

- Male-to-male sexual contact (41%)
- Hemophilia (27%)
- Injection drug use (10%)
- Heterosexual contact (8%)
- Male-to-male sexual contact and injection drug use (6%)
- Other/not identified (4%)
- Transfusion recipient (4%)

Notes

Adolescents / Youth and AIDS (continued)

- In the U.S., in 2002, 65% of reported AIDS cases in 13–19 year-olds were black (15% of adolescent population is black). Hispanics accounted for 16% of reported AIDS cases.
- Most 13–19 year-old female adolescents reported contracting HIV followed by AIDS through heterosexual contact (66%), injection drug use (19%), and other/not identified (15%).
- HIV is spreading rapidly among younger urban gay males who are too young to recall the beginning of the AIDS epidemic two decades ago at alarming rates.

Adolescents / Youth and AIDS (continued)

- Adolescents who are most vulnerable to HIV infection include homeless or runaways, juvenile offenders, and school dropouts.
- Worldwide, sexual intercourse is by far the most common mode of HIV transmission.
- In the U.S., as many as half of all new HIV infections are now associated either directly or indirectly with injection drug use (i.e., injecting with an HIV-contaminated needle or having sex with an HIV-infected drug user) (Body Health Resources Corporation 2004).

Drug Use in the Entertainment Industry

- Alcohol appeared in 93% of movies, 17% of songs; tobacco appeared in 89% of movies.
- Sixty-three percent of rap songs contained reference to substances.
- In movies depicting illicit drugs, marijuana appeared most frequently (51%); hallucinogens, heroin and other opiates, and miscellaneous others (each 12%); and crack cocaine (2%).

Notes

_____

_____

_____

_____

_____

_____

_____

_____

_____

_____

_____

_____

_____

_____

_____

_____

_____

_____

_____

_____

_____

_____

_____

_____

Prescription Drugs and Illicit Drugs *via* the Internet

- Drug sales are booming online. Prescription drugs are being advertised and sold without a prescription over the Internet, often in the form of SPAM emailings. Approximately 90% of online drug sales take place without a medical prescription (Join Together Online and BBC News, 2005).

- Numerous web sites are used by a growing number of drug users as forums for learning and exchanging the latest information and techniques about drug use (i.e., purchasing equipment for growing, chat rooms sharing information about the use of illicit drugs, news and information about drug "get togethers"—such as parties, raves, festival locations where drugs are prevalent).

CHAPTER 17

Drug Abuse Prevention

The chapter outline provides you with an organizational guide to the topics and ideas presented in this chapter of the text.

◎ Key Terms

Define the following terms:

1. AOD _____

2. ATOD _____

3. Scare tactic approach _____

4. Alternatives approach _____

◎ Fill-in-the-Blank

1. The _____ is a national and

 international association of college and university peer education programs focused on alcohol abuse

 prevention and other related student health and safety issues.

2. A _____ is a court designed to focus on treatment

 programs and options in place of punishment for drug offenders.

3. _____ is a state of consciousness in which there is a constant

 level of awareness focusing on one object.

◎ Identify

1. Identify the three levels of drug prevention programs and indicate the audience at which each is aimed.

 a. _____

 b. _____

 c. _____

2. Identify five categories of drug users.

 a. _____

 b. _____

 c. _____

 d. _____

 e. _____

3. Identify three family-based protective factors that can insulate against drug use.

 a. _____

 b. _____

 c. _____

4. Identify and describe four models of drug prevention in higher education.

 a. _____

 b. _____

 c. _____

 d. _____

◎ Discussion Questions

1. How do school-based drug prevention programs attempt to prevent drug abuse? What topics and questions do they address? What tactics do they employ? Are these programs effective? _____

_____

_____

_____

2. What do family-based drug prevention programs need to do in order to effectively prevent drug use? __

_____

_____

_____

3. How can student peers be involved in helping to prevent drug use on college campuses? _____

_____

_____

_____

4. Has the DARE program been effective in preventing drug use? Explain. _____

_____

_____

_____

Notes

_____

_____

_____

_____

_____

_____

_____

_____

_____

_____

_____

_____

_____

_____

_____

_____

_____

_____

_____

_____

_____

_____

_____

_____

NINTH EDITION

Glen R. Hanson
Peter J. Venturelli
Annette E. Fleckenstein

Drugs and Society

Drug Abuse Prevention

Chapter 17

Levels of Drug Prevention

Level 1—Primary Prevention

- **Primary drug prevention programs** refer to the very broad range of activities aimed at reducing the risk of drug use among non-users and assuring continued nonuse. Often targeted to at-risk neighborhoods, communities, and families.

Level 1—Primary Prevention Programs

- **Intrapersonal factors**
  - Affective education, values clarification, personal and social skills development (assertiveness and refusal skills), drug information and education
- **Small group factors**
  - Peer mentoring, conflict resolution, curriculum infusion, clarification of peer norms, alternatives, strengthening families
- **Systems level**
  - Strengthening school-family links, school-community links, and community support systems, media advocacy efforts, reduce alcohol marketing

Notes

Levels of Drug Prevention
(continued)

Level 2—Secondary Prevention
- **Secondary drug prevention programs** target at-risk groups, *early* experimenters and abuse populations in order to stop the progression to drugs of abuse (similar to "early intervention")

Level 2—Secondary Drug Prevention Programs

- Assessment strategies: identification of abuse subgroups and individual diagnoses
- Early intervention coupled with sanctions
- Teacher-counselor-parent team approach
- Developing healthy alternative youth culture
- Use of recovering role models

Levels of Drug Prevention
(continued)

Level 3—Tertiary Prevention
- **Tertiary drug prevention** is intervention at an advanced state of drug use/abuse. Very similar to drug abuse treatment.

Notes

Level 3—Tertiary Prevention Programs

- Assessment and diagnosis
- Referral to treatment
- Case management
- Reentry

The Critical Importance of Considering the Type of Audience and Approach

Audiences Differ with Regard to Drug Use:
- Nonusers
- Early experimenters of drugs
- Non-problem-drug users—those who abuse drugs on occasion, mostly for recreation purposes
- Nondetected, committed, or secret users—those who abuse drugs and have no interest in stopping
- Problem users
- Former users

Comprehensive Prevention Programs for Drug Use and Abuse

Q. What are some of the unique characteristics/examples of the following?
- Harm Reduction Model
- Community-Based Prevention
- School-Based Drug Prevention
- Family-Based Prevention Programs

Notes

Answers to Previous Slide

Harm Reduction: Practiced in Netherlands and in the United Kingdom. Meets addicts on their own level. Uses an "open door" policy. Addicts are encouraged to take part in prevention and treatment services.

Community-Based Prevention: Provide coordinated programs among many agencies and organizations involved in prevention.

School-Based Prevention: Drug education in elementary, junior high, senior high, and college level.

Family-Based Prevention: Stresses the quality of parent-child interaction, communication skill, child management practices, and family management.

Drug Education Strategies

- Strategies that focus on and provide drug use/ abuse information
- Strategies that stress non-drug-use values, beliefs, and attitudes
- Strategies that emphasize the consequences of drug use (namely, warnings and scare tactics about drug abuse)

Major Drug Prevention Strategies

1. **Scare Tactic Approach**—drug prevention information based on emphasizing the extreme negative effects of drug use by coercing/ warning the audience about the dangers of drug use.

2. **Information-Only or Awareness Model**—assumes that teaching about the harmful effects of drugs will change attitudes about use and abuse.

Notes

_____

_____

_____

_____

_____

_____

_____

_____

_____

_____

_____

_____

_____

_____

_____

_____

_____

_____

_____

_____

_____

_____

Major Drug Prevention Strategies
(continued)

3. **Attitude change model or affective education model**—assumes people use drugs because of a lack of self-esteem and other personality factors.
4. **Social influences model**—assumes that drug users lack resistance skills. Examples include teaching skills to resist drug use.
5. **Ecological or Person-in-Environment Model**—focuses on the causes of drug use resulting largely from the social environment (drug use and abuse problems among the young are social).

Major Drug Prevention Strategies
(continued)

Major prevention strategies include:

1. dissemination of drug information
2. cognitive and behavioral skills training for youth, parents, and professionals, and mass media
3. mass media programming
4. grass roots citizen participation
5. leadership training
6. policy analysis and reformulation

Making Drug Education Programs More Effective

- Practice deliberate planning
- Review the previous history
- Establish links between the messages conveyed and learned and other aspects of students' life experiences
- Effectively promote programs
- Properly allocate resources
- Constantly evaluate effectiveness of program

Examples of Current Large-Scale Drug Prevention Programs

- **Bacchus and Gamma Peer Education Network**—found on college campuses, promotes socializing without alcohol use.
- **D.A.R.E.** (Drug Abuse Resistance Education)—school-based drug education programs by law enforcement officials.
- **Drug Courts**—courts designed to focus on *treatment programs* and options instead of purely jailing drug offenders. Criminal justice collaborates and shares power with substance abuse treatment community members in rendering verdicts (decisions) regarding outcome of drug charges.

Other Alternatives to Drug Use

- Alternatives approach
  - An approach emphasizing the exploration of positive alternatives to drug abuse, based on replacing the pleasurable feelings experienced from drug use with involvement in social and educational activities. Examples include athletics, exercise, hiking, cultivating hobbies, mountain climbing, and getting involved in other physically or mentally challenging alternatives.
- Meditation
  - A state of consciousness in which there is a constant level of awareness focusing on one object; for example, getting involved in yoga and/or Zen Buddhism.

Notes

CHAPTER 18

Treating Drug Dependence

The chapter outline provides you with an organizational guide to the topics and ideas presented in this chapter of the text.

◎ Key Terms

Define the following terms:

1. Open meetings _____

2. Closed meetings _____

3. Therapeutic community _____

4. Agonist _____

5. Antagonist _____

6. Patient placement criteria _____

◎ Identify

1. Identify five of the thirteen NIDA principles that characterize effective addiction treatment.

a. _____

b. _____

c. _____

d. _____

e. _____

2. Identify and discuss three general therapeutic drug treatment strategies.

a. _____

b. _____

c. _____

3. Identify and discuss three therapeutic approaches that may be used to supplement or enhance existing drug treatment programs, according to NIDA.

a. _____

b. _____

c. _____

◎ Discussion Questions

1. Why is it difficult to assess the success of Alcoholics Anonymous? _____

_____

_____

_____

2. Describe the Minnesota Model of drug treatment. _____

_____

_____

_____

3. How are pharmacological strategies used to treat drug abuse? Give two examples of these therapies.___

_____

_____

_____

4. What requirements must one fulfill in order to become a certified addiction counselor? _____

_____

_____

_____

Notes

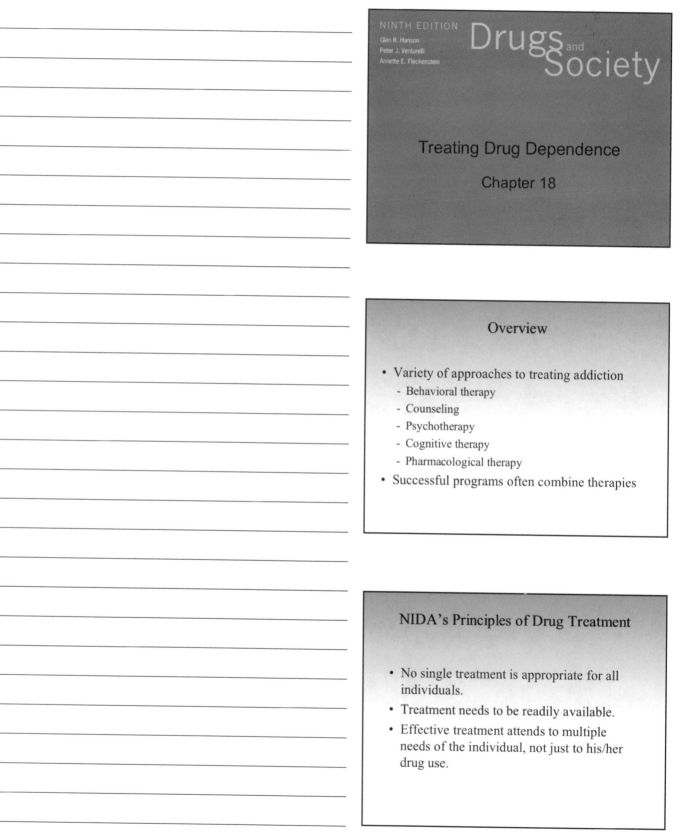

NINTH EDITION
Glen R. Hanson
Peter J. Venturelli
Annette E. Fleckenstein

Drugs and **Society**

Treating Drug Dependence

Chapter 18

Overview

- Variety of approaches to treating addiction
  - Behavioral therapy
  - Counseling
  - Psychotherapy
  - Cognitive therapy
  - Pharmacological therapy
- Successful programs often combine therapies

NIDA's Principles of Drug Treatment

- No single treatment is appropriate for all individuals.
- Treatment needs to be readily available.
- Effective treatment attends to multiple needs of the individual, not just to his/her drug use.

Notes

NIDA's Principles of Drug Treatment
(continued)

- An individual's treatment plan must be assessed continually.
- Remaining in treatment for an adequate period is critical.
- Counseling and other behavioral therapies are critical.

NIDA's Principles of Drug Treatment
(continued)

- Medications are important for many patients.
- Addicted or drug-abusing individuals with co-existing mental disorders should have both disorders treated.
- Medical detoxification is only the first step.
- Treatment does not need to be voluntary to be effective.

NIDA's Principles of Drug Treatment
(continued)

- Possible drug use during treatment must be monitored continuously.
- Treatment programs should provide assessment for other diseases.
- Recovery can be a long-term process and frequently requires multiple episodes of treatment.

Notes

_____

_____

_____

_____

_____

_____

_____

_____

_____

_____

_____

_____

_____

_____

_____

_____

_____

_____

_____

_____

_____

_____

_____

_____

_____

Historical Approaches

- Alcoholics Anonymous
  - Open and closed meetings

- Rehabilitation facilities
  - "Twelve-stepping"
  - Minnesota Model

Other General Strategies

- Medical detoxification
- Outpatient drug-free treatment
- Short-term residential
- Long-term residential
- Criminal justice-involved abusers

Specific Therapeutic Strategies

- Relapse prevention
- The Matrix Model
- Supportive-expressive psychotherapy
- Individualized drug counseling
- Motivational enhancement therapy
- Community reinforcement/vouchers

Notes

Examples of Pharmacological Strategies

- Opioid agonist maintenance therapy
- Nicotine replacement therapy
- Antagonist therapy (e.g., naloxone)
- Other examples (e.g., clonidine, disulfiram)

Drug Addiction Treatment Act of 2000

- Subutex and Suboxone
- Drugs can be prescribed in an office setting
- Provides greater patient access to treatment

Current Trends in Providing Treatment

- Certifying qualified counselors
  - Responsibilities include screening candidates, patient education, developing treatment plans, understanding pharmacology
- Patient placement criteria
- Special focus programs